# MIND FLIGHT

# MIND
# FLIGHT

LISA WHELAN & SETO OGALI

Matador
9 Priory Business Park,
Wistow Road, Kibworth Beauchamp,
Leicestershire. LE8 0RX
Tel: (+44) 116 279 2299
Fax: (+44) 116 279 2277
Email: books@troubador.co.uk
Web: www.troubador.co.uk/matador

ISBN 978 1784622 732

British Library Cataloguing in Publication Data.
A catalogue record for this book is available from the British Library.

Printed and bound in the UK by TJ International, Padstow, Cornwall
Typeset in 11pt Aldine401 BT Roman by Troubador Publishing Ltd, Leicester, UK

**Matador** is an imprint of Troubador Publishing Ltd

*It is simple, don't complicate it!*

*This book is dedicated to Hratch Ogali
and Dennis Whelan who gave the blessing
of unconditional love.*

CHAPTER 1

# Death is our only certainty

The sound of the intercom clicks.

"Ladies and gentlemen, I would like to welcome you aboard the Mind Flight plane, my name is Scarlet and I will be looking after you for the duration of your flight. If you could please make sure all your belongings are placed into the overhead lockers and your seatbelts are securely fastened for take off, as we endeavour to embark on our journey to the last frontier.

"I would like you to take a moment to imagine everything in your past is gone, nothing exists but the now, this present moment.

"For this special time that you have here, I would like you to think about you. About your life, about the story you are creating, about the life you want and lastly how the life you are leading affects those around you.

"Ask yourself this question: if your life were a film, would you want to watch that film?"

1

The passengers glance at each other, there is a discomfort in the cabin, a reluctance to listen, there is a sense of detachment that takes hold of many of the passengers. Some laugh apprehensively.

The comforting sound of seatbelts fastening, overhead lockers locking, snippets of confused conversation resound throughout the cabin as the passengers of Mind Flight A570 prepare to settle for the journey ahead.

Molly rummages in the seat pocket in front of her, her tangled tassels swinging from her brown suede poncho mimicking her skittish nature. Pulling out a safety card she glances at the pictures on it. The pictures look back at her, the same pictures she has seen on every aircraft she has ever been on; the type of pictures that you glance at quickly so that your mind doesn't think too much on actually being in the situation described, where in reality you have to partake in one of those horrifying emergency positions. She flips the card over, looking on the back. The title that stares back at her takes her by surprise.

'Safety for Life'

She browses the headings... Breath, Mind, Emotions, Depression, Birth, Love, Fear, and Death. She begins to read...

'Death is the only certainty we have in life, why be afraid of it?'

She quickly places the card back into the pocket in front of her squeezing the hand of the man sitting next to her. The unshaven man who appears to have invested more in his clothing than his looks. The cool dishevelled look. He doesn't take his eyes from the menu that he is studying. She moves his hand. He turns giving her one of his familiar 'now what!' looks of exasperation.

"What's the matter?" she asks.

"Most of it looks edible. Although there are a couple of weird things." He points to the menu.

Molly glances at the words that stare back at her. 'Water with a splash of lemon. Who can deny the cleansing properties of this combination, perfect for the mind, the brain and the body?' 'Doughnuts – indulge in the richness and glory of one of these delicious doughnuts, feel the bliss and luxury of heaven in the clouds.' She looks to Jake smiling.

"I like the sound of the doughnuts and the flowers are lovely!" Molly states with a hint of childlike enthusiasm.

The cabin is as white as the first day of snowfall. The seats' leather trimmed with pale blue, lit by ambient blue lighting. On each table sits a single white tulip. A simple white tag hangs from the small triangular shaped vase seated in a circular holder to the right hand side of the seat. Molly picks up the tulip and reads the message 'renewal'. She smiles and glances to Jake's seat. Jake is rummaging through the seat back in front of him. Molly leans across studying his tag: 'rebirth', she smiles.

Jake glances as he hunts for his headset for the TV.

"Have you got your headset?"

"Look what it says, rebirth, that's what the white tulip means."

Jake pauses for a moment, shakes his head and continues to hunt for the headset.

"There are no TVs," Molly whispers.

"What?"

"There are no TVs," Molly giggles.

"Don't be ridiculous."

"I'm telling you there is no entertainment."

"Well what are we supposed to do for the next thirteen hours?"

"Talk maybe?" Molly giggles.

Jake rings the call bell. Scarlet makes her way through the cabin, her pillbox hat sits tilted to the left, her blonde hair swept up into the perfect pleat. The pale blue uniform enhancing her soft blue eyes as she gracefully makes her way to calm his irate buzzing,

"Yes can I help you sir?"

"Am I correct in thinking that there are no TVs?"

"That's correct sir," she answers.

"Oh!"

"We don't have TVs on any of the Mind Flight aircraft."

"Well what are we supposed to do for the next thirteen hours?"

She smiles. "Don't worry sir there will be plenty for you to do."

Another bell rings calling for her attention.

"I'm sorry sir I have to attend to another passenger."

Jake looks to Molly with a look of disgust as he opens the flap in the seat in front of him. He pulls out a booklet. A plain white glossy embossed booklet; across the front are engraved in pale blue the words 'The sky is the limit…

write your reality'. He turns it over and his name greets him, beautifully engraved in pale blue silk stitching.

"How much did this cost? Look, they can engrave my name but they can't provide TVs."

He opens the book and on the front page there is a question. 'If your life were a film would you want to watch that film? If not, why not?' He flicks through the remainder of the book only to be met by blank white pages.

"If my life were a film, I would delete this day. What possessed you to book with this airline?"

Molly's eyes are fixed on the window, looking out across the many runways that lead to the many different destinations. The different aircraft making their way around the course in front of them with one aim, without halt to reach the finish line in the quickest time possible. Her view is supported by the background sound of seatbelts fastening mixed with the rumble of voices throughout the cabin as it gently fades to silent anticipation, as quiet as the silence that follows heavy snowfall. The only sound that can be heard is the soothing rumble of the engines, taxiing towards the runway.

The sound of the intercom clicks. "It is time to begin your journey, the journey is yours and yours alone. We have one life, no re-runs, all we have is now and it is time for you to make now matter."

# CHAPTER 2

# Comfortable in an Uncomfortable Situation

The light creeps into view as the aircraft vibrates along the runway, the never-ending runway. The runway that leads to our destiny, to our future, forwards into the unknown. Captain Dennis has one aim, to lift before time runs out, for with Mind Flight A570 take off only happens at the last minute when there is no runway left.

The passengers gaze out of the window aware that the runway is reaching its end. There are a few nervous faces; a couple of reassuring giggles and a handful of scattered hands grasping their arm rests.

Molly points out of the window. Jake's hand is on his head in despair at the journey ahead. The dotted lights glisten in the morning sunrise as they guide us to the path, the path to our destiny.

Captain Dennis' hands grasp the controls, holding steady as he pushes forwards on the throttle. The runway lights flash past, they are running away as they lift into the air, into the clouds, into the surrounding sky that sits silent, secure, strong. A sky that knows its purpose, it knows its path, it knows that it is there to guide everything that lays beneath it; its purpose to enable life on Earth to evolve and flourish.

It is all in the starting point; it is in making the decision to go, to embrace, to enjoy and to embark without fear into the unknown. The wheels lift off and the runway disappears beneath them. As they turn, the horizon is their focus as they leave land behind for a vast ocean, like glass shimmering in the sunlight.

Molly glances to the left, the wings are flexing upwards at the weight of the plane. The sunlight reflects off of the wing blinding her. The crescent moon sits to the right hand side of the sun; he rests as he allows her to take his place in the sky. She waits patiently revealing a little more of herself on every turn, her warmth is welcoming the world beneath, the world that is waiting to see if she is going to shine, like a beacon lighting the way for all who are lost in the vast ocean below.

Molly reaches for the white book that is sitting in the seat cover in front of her. She opens the book. 'What will your film be?' She glances to the left, the clear sky where there is nothing and there is everything out there. The pale blue backdrop lends a fitting canvas for the painting that is to be created, a canvas of infinite possibility.

The passengers begin to rummage through the pockets of the seats in front of them. Searching for in-flight magazines, duty free catalogues and their entertainment for the flight. An array of lights light up the cabin as the call attendance buzzer, buzzes one after the other.

The intercom clicks.

"Good morning!' There is a long pause… "My name is Captain Dennis and I will be escorting you on your journey down to Alaska today." His voice is a rich baritone with the smooth silky gentleness that only an accent can bring. The type of accent that isn't quite distinguishable, but one that is so beautiful, there is no desire to reveal its source. "I'm joined here today on the flight deck by my co pilot Miss Jenson, and a very obliging first officer Douglas Carter. I would like to take this opportunity to introduce you to my co-pilot Miss Jenson."

"Hello everyone," a young woman's voice resonates over the antenna.

"Don't worry she is only the co-pilot. I have complete control of the plane."

An infectious chuckle runs through the aircraft.

"Well at least we know he has some idea what he's doing." Molly gives Jake a disapproving glance.

"The flight will take approximately thirteen hours, we will be cruising at 35,000 feet and travelling at approximately 500 miles per hour.

"Depending on clear whether conditions, our flight will take us over some beautiful scenic areas such as Iceland, Greenland and northern Canada. Make sure you get a chance to catch a glimpse of some of the spectacular scenes beneath us.

"It is the most beautiful place in the world up here. As on all journeys the seasons become our surroundings as our environment makes us who we are. To visit the sky in springtime is like feeling life in every breath."

There is a long silent pause supported by the sound of a satisfied exhalation as he continues…

"Spring is our beginning, it is the start of our journey. It is the coming to life, as those born in spring contain the energy of a new beginning. The springing forth of life into a new chapter, like a flower coming into blossom. With water and air, it comes to life, it flourishes. Its colours are magnificent, vibrant, even sometimes blinding. When it has attention nothing can stop it shining, but if it is starved of light and water it will wilt and die. Spring needs attention, it needs light, to bring life.

"The sun's warmth radiates to the cotton candy clouds above giving them the glow of the gentlest peach blossom. Like each cloud has been lit, to lead the way, like stepping stones through a tranquil lake into summer.

"Summer is the part of the journey where things are pleasurable and challenging in equal measure as for those born in summer like the flowers that come to life in spring they have the heat of the sun, that they must protect themselves. They do not know when the rain will come, they are cautious, if they reveal themselves for too long they are sure to burn. Unlike spring's urgency, summer has its reservations. The wind begins to blow as the petals fall, the leaves float to the earth for renewal.

"Autumn is a time of letting go. Those born in autumn

are naked, and free, they are open to whatever comes as they know winter is on its way; they have no fear for they are already bare. It is the time between autumn and winter when everything falls silent, when we are in the depths of change. A change that creeps up on us, we are there in the silence of winter; it is the part of the journey where thinking begins.

"Those born in winter are the thinkers. The snow falls as winter emerges. It is time for hibernation and it is time to retreat; it is the time to think, to reflect and to reassess. It is the darkness before the light, nature is telling us to think, to see where we have been and to reveal to us where we are going, to move forward into the future with new energy, new power and new strength in preparation for the next chapter."

Molly sits watching the sunrise lost in the world outside her window, for a moment the captain's voice fades into the background as her mind drifts to the sky of serenity as it encompasses all that she has heard as nature unfolds before her very eyes. She replays the words spoken by the captain over in her mind... 'We emerge from the hibernation of the winter months, the thinking time and evolve into the time of action. The sun awakens. It is a new beginning, it is time to bring everything to life.' Spring the time of her birth. The thought of life, her life, brings her back to the present moment, as Captain Dennis' final words greet her.

"Our flight today will be taking us out over Hudson Bay all the way over the eastern part of Canada into Canadian airspace. Finally making our approach into

Alaska arriving at Alaska at approximately 7 pm local time. Scarlet, our angel of the skies, will be looking after you throughout the flight today, so please feel free to ask her if you need anything.

"For those of you who haven't flown Mind Flight before, this will feel unusual, but this is normal for first time flyers. I can promise you, it will be like nothing you have experienced before, but one that I guarantee you will be able to embark on by yourself by the end of the flight. If you do nothing else today please make sure you have some doughnuts, they are quite amazing. On behalf of Mind Flight airlines please sit back, be comfortable and enjoy the ride."

Molly looks a little anxious, she glances at the note on her flower in front of her. 'Eternal Life'. She takes the flower, handing it to Jake. She waves the tag in front of him. He hits back as if swatting an irritating fly. Molly looks around the cabin. There is a mumble of conversation, of excitement and anticipation mixed with fear as passengers glance at the books, some pick them up and close them, some stare out of the window, others communicate their disgust at the lack of entertainment. She picks up the pen, biting the tip as she stares at the empty page.

The intercom clicks as Scarlet's voice resounds throughout the cabin. "Ladies and gentlemen, I would like to welcome you all to the magic that is the sky! I think it is very important for you to know that I will put my life on the line for you, in every possible way that I can, but there is one exception if the captain falls asleep as he has a tendency to do. I can assure you I will be the first person out of that door."

A raucous applaud like laughter resounds through the cabin. Scarlet giggles a mischievous childlike giggle; there is something angelic yet cheeky about her disposition. The words she speaks appear a world away from her appearance.

"If you would like to look in your seat pockets in front of you, you will find a few things that you will need for the journey. It will be your own minds that will keep you entertained throughout the duration of the flight today.

"Think of this journey as a birth, as a new beginning. Think of it as everything coming to life, all the restrictions are gone, there are no demands, there are no thoughts. There is a letting go of the old to make way for the new. It is a new beginning."

The seat belt signs turn off. Jake sighs, unclipping his belt and standing, desperate to get to the overhead lockers before anyone else does. He pushes the locker button and nothing happens. He pulls at it but the locker won't open. He bends down reaching for the flight attendant buzzer, looking down the aircraft, desperate to express the words that are churning around in his head.

Scarlet walks towards him, she is interrupted by several passengers on the way as Jake's patience is withering. "Yes, can I help you sir?"

"There is something wrong with my overhead locker, it won't open."

Scarlet places her hand on his shoulder. "It's ok sir your belongings are locked away safely for the flight."

"No you don't understand, I want my laptop."

"Unfortunately, we won't be able to access any of the equipment until we land sir."

Jake stares with a sense of disbelief.

"I'm sorry sir."

"I have a business to run."

"I'm sure with your level of dedication sir it won't collapse in thirteen hours. Sometimes it's good to let go for a little while."

The attendance buzzers are flashing throughout the cabin. Scarlet makes her way through the cabin of passengers like prisoners demanding their release as they attempt to access their belongings, picking up the handset she addresses her passengers.

"Ladies and gentlemen, please do not worry about your items they will be available to you when we land. I know how inconvenient it is, when I first boarded this aircraft I also found it difficult letting go of the things that I had become so attached to; but after a while you begin to realize that there is a freedom in letting go, a liberation even, if only for a few hours. You have no choice but to accept the situation. If you need my assistance on anything else I am happy to assist but if you could kindly refrain from discussing this matter any further."

Silence falls throughout the cabin. A man stands. Others follow shouting their disapproval. Scarlet picks up the handset again.

"Ladies and gentlemen, please return to your seats. We will not be landing any time soon, we are over the Atlantic Ocean and it is impossible if you want to live. If you want life please remain seated." Her tone is firm but gentle.

"I want to speak to the captain," says the standing man, "and I want to speak to him now! We want him to land this aircraft this instance. This is insanity, we are not your prisoners."

"Good morning!"

There is a long silent pause. The man is ranting as in a 1920's silent movie, his lips are moving but his words are meaningless as the silence is more powerful than his profanities.

The voice over the intercom instructs. "Could the gentleman who is sitting in seat number seven, please press the silver button that is situated on the left hand side of your seat. I will be able to hear you clearly as will all of the other passengers on the aircraft." His voice is gentle, slow and calm.

The man furiously looks for the button; he is still standing as his finger presses the button repeatedly.

Scarlet walks towards him gently guiding his hand away as she holds her perfectly manicured fingernail on the buzzer for a couple of seconds until the light switches on. She places her hand on his shoulder and gestures for him to sit down in the chair. He snatches his shoulder away as if she is infected with some fatal disease. He sits down clearing his throat as he begins to speak.

"We want to land this aircraft."

There is a long pause.

"Why?"

The man laughs in disbelief.

"You have no right to do this. What is this a hijack?"

He is met by silence.

The man sits silent for a moment. He sits with a disgruntled look upon his face before continuing his performance.

"We want to use our laptops and phones."

"Sir, I would ask you to use this as a lesson to focus on learning to be comfortable in an uncomfortable situation. This will serve you much better in life than paying attention to what you can't have. I assure you this is not a hijack situation and I will get you to your destination as quickly as I can, at which point you can resume contact with the world beneath us. Embrace the silence for you have no choice in the matter. It is simple, don't complicate it as you have no control over it."

"I don't like your attitude or the attitude of your staff." He takes a momentary breath. "Everyone wants their items. It's ridiculous!"

"Scarlet?" the captain's voice instructs softly. "Scarlet, can you please give everyone some breakfast."

In the moments that follow his instruction it feels as if a wave of un-comfortableness has been washed over the cabin, a hint of serenity seated at its core. She nods. The gentleman sits, his head bowed as he looks into his lap. Scarlet makes her way through the cabin.

Jake reaches his hand out to attract her attention.

"Yes sir, can I help you?"

"Do you have a blanket?"

"Yes, certainly sir, give me a second and I will get one for you."

He turns to Molly.

"At least they have a blanket."

"Don't get too excited, you haven't seen it yet."

Scarlet returns with the most beautiful pale blue cashmere dressing gown blanket with a silk pillow attached.

"Wow!" Molly cannot contain her excitement as she runs her hands across the fabric. "Where do you get these from they are so beautiful?"

"They are specially made for us, we believe sleep is one of the most important things we can do and one that needs luxury and comfort."

She turns the blanket over to look at the delicate stitching sewn on the back. The words 'sleep is your friend' stare back.

Jake laughs.

"At least they have got something right."

Scarlet smiles as she leaves.

Molly is lost in the orange and red landscape. The clouds perform the perfect wave like formation, like a beautifully crafted painting, there is an unreality about it, an unreality in the reality of its pure perfection.

She turns to look at Jake who is wrapped up in the blanket, his head tilted to the side, his hands covering his face with his eyes closed. She smiles at the thought of him looking like a hamster snuggling into his cotton wool. She glances back; the colours have changed tone from orange to crimson. A crimson masked with cumulus cloud formations, working together to create the day ahead.

The presence of dawn prompts the premier that daylight will always follow. A dimension where all living creatures that are ruled by the sun awaken; to beings that create their own dusk as they close their eyes waiting for the magic of dawn to return once again.

Jake leans on Molly's shoulder closing his eyes.

Her mind is transfixed on what the landscape has to offer; she is lost in her thoughts and in the words of Captain Dennis. 'It is simple, don't complicate it.'

He looks up at her for help as he covers himself in the blanket resting his head on the pillow.

"Now all I need is a TV."

# CHAPTER 3

# Breath is Life

The young girl sits crying, her hands trembling.

"I can't breathe."

The man next to her presses the flight attendant buzzer.

"I want to get off."

Scarlet makes her way through the aircraft, she smiles along the way asking the passengers if they are ok, some smile back, others don't acknowledge her existence but she smiles all the same.

"Yes sir how can I help you?"

"This young lady isn't feeling very well."

The young girl sits shaking uncontrollably, consumed by fear.

"Sir, may I ask if you could kindly take a seat at the back of the aircraft while I help the young lady."

The young man gets up. Scarlet sits down and takes her hand. Concert wristbands decorate her arms, her mane like curly brunette hair conceals her face. Scarlet gently pulls her hair back.

"Tell me?"

The young girl begins to sob, the other passengers on the aircraft are aware of the commotion as it spreads through the cabin; others make their way to the toilet to get a glimpse of the action.

"I... I don't know I just feel so scared. I can't breathe." Her breaths are short and shallow.

"It's ok. I want you to listen to me." Scarlet's voice changes from angelic to authoritative.

She takes her finger and gently places it in the centre of the young girl's forehead. The young girl's thoughts are the tears on her tissue, the tissue in her hand that she is picking to pieces, the tissue that is being passed from one hand to the other hoping for a way out of this situation, trapped in a void of emotions.

"I want you to focus here, focus on the little black screen in the centre of your forehead, and I want you to breathe into here, imagine the breath going into here. In through the nose and out through the mouth."

The young girl tries but her breaths are shallow.

"More, I want you to breathe in every bit of air that you have, as if breath is everything, you want it and you want it now."

The young girl breathes in; her last breath shakes as the adjustment is taking place.

"Good girl! Good girl! That's it."

She breathes again.

"In through the nose and out through the mouth."

Breathe.

"And again."

Breathe.

"One more."

Breathe.

"And again."

The girl's facial expression shows her desire and desperation for breath.

"It's ok you may feel a little dizzy, that's ok you are bringing everything to life, you are just giving your system a shake up."

The young girl begins to calm as Scarlet places the palm of her hand on the young girl's forehead, all of a sudden the young girl's body shifts and drops deeper into her chair. Her arms steady and the tissue is released from her grasp.

"Now I want you to close your eyes and keep breathing. This time on your out breath I want you to say the words 'new life, power and strength'. I want you to feel them with every ounce of passion that you have inside of you, demand them, demand from your mind. New life, power and strength.

"Make your thought objective, you want it and you want it now. Instruct your mind to give you energy, the mind's purpose is to bring life, ask and it will give you what you need." Scarlet breathes in unison with the young girl.

"Now I want you to slowly open your eyes."

As the young girl opens her eyes everything is calm, her hands have stopped shaking, the tears have stopped, the scene is calmness and clarity. She looks up and Scarlet's smile greets her, as she reveals her innocent beauty.

"Remember the deep breath on its own does absolutely nothing but when you make it objective with instruction and you breathe into here," she places her finger in the centre of the young girl's forehead, "you switch everything on, everything comes to life."

Several of the passengers have witnessed the transformation; some look away embarrassed, others are intrigued, and some really couldn't care less. The young girl smiles, her disposition is naturally coy and apologetic. Scarlet reaches out to hug her, she holds her for a few seconds.

"Give your mind the right instruction and it will give the brain and the body more power and greater energy. When we alter how we instruct ourselves we alter our behaviour. Take time to seek within your own mind and you will be able to instruct it to create the change."

"I can't live without him." The young girl's eyes fill with tears.

"It's ok." Scarlet strokes the young girl's hair.

"I love him, I can't live without him."

"As quickly as things change one way they can change back just as quickly. Your meeting with him will have been for a purpose, you may not see that purpose now but in time all will be revealed to you. People come into your life, they create an energy, they bring you what you need at the time, they serve a purpose, some stay with us for a lifetime and some depart. They will stay for as long as you need it. One day you will know that he wasn't supposed to stay and the reason why."

Scarlet takes the young girl's notepad and places it in front of her.

"Write, you will find your answer."

The young girl smiles; there is an uncertainty in her eyes. She picks up the notepad and pen and begins to write.

Scarlet gently touches her hand. "Focus on the things that give you strength not weakness. When we are anxious all thought goes out of the window and we lose our way, we become blind we cannot see clearly and we feel as though we are unable to function.

"To create the shift we need action. For when we act we move forwards, forwards out of the stagnant situation that we are in. When you don't want to take action that is the time you need to do it the most. Do that little exercise and it will all change, you will see it differently. I promise you, your grief will turn to growth."

The young girl's mouth smiles but her eyes are still engaged in the turmoil that is going on in her heart.

Scarlet reaches out gently placing her hand onto her leg.

"I know you don't believe me right now, but I promise you one day, if you do this, you will.

Stay strong!"

# CHAPTER 4

# You have a Beautiful Imagination

The middle-aged woman glances towards Scarlet as she quickly makes her way into the bathroom closing the door behind her. She double-checks the lock as she reaches into the inside of her jacket pocket, pulling out what looks like a small bottle of perfume. She looks into the mirror, her bloodshot eyes complementing her flushed complexion. She removes the lid and takes a lawless swig, gasping at the blissful buzz as it hits her brain. She looks into the mirror, closing her eyes as she exhales, a breath of calmness; she smiles at herself as she proceeds to gulp down the remainder of the contents in the bottle. She throws the empty bottle into the bin, takes out her toothbrush and a small tube of toothpaste. She cleans her teeth, re-applies her lipstick, runs her fingers through her auburn hair, straightens her jacket and opens the door.

As the door opens Scarlet stands firm. The woman smiles briefly, looking down to the floor. Scarlet moves to the left preventing her escape.

"Can we have a little chat?" Scarlet asks with a smile.

"I'm sorry, I really don't like flying, I would prefer it if I could just return to my seat."

"It will only take five minutes."

There is a young man waiting to use the toilet. Scarlet turns to him and smiles. She enters the toilet, removes the empty bottle from the bin and closes the door behind her.

"May I ask what was in here?" The middle-aged lady looks shocked. Scarlet pauses. "You drank from it in the bathroom."

"What are you talking about?"

"I'm here to help you."

"I just needed some air, some space. I don't like flying."

"I know what it's like living in that world where your life is swinging like a pendulum. It's either up here or down there and when you take that sip of drink it stays in the middle. It stays calm and in that place everything is ok, there is balance."

"Look I'm terribly sorry, I really don't know what you are talking about. Now can I please go back to my seat, please?"

"I won't be able to allow you to do that again."

The middle-aged woman pretends she doesn't hear that comment.

Scarlet places her hand onto her shoulder holding it there for a few seconds before speaking.

"It's ok, it will all be ok. I promise you it will be ok."

The woman glances, there is a look in her eyes that says that she wants it to be ok but that is only for a fleeting moment.

"You search everyday for that space of calm between the high and the low, that space where nothing can touch you, that place where you are at peace, that place exists elsewhere and not where you think it is."

The woman's hands are shaking.

"It doesn't bring you the calm that you think because chaos follows, the secrets, the lies, the fear."

The woman stands as she grips the handle of the door.

"The thinking. The thinking it becomes too much, most people who drink they are the creative ones, they are the ones that see beyond, the ones with beautiful imaginations. When the imagination is left to wander, they lose themselves, they feel lost and alone. The drink numbs the thinking.

"You have a beautiful gift. The gift of an incredible imagination. Focus on it, enhance it, use it, create the life that you see, the life that you know is possible and it is possible, create it from this place of calm, that is fearless, that has all the love you could possibly imagine in the world.

"That is the place that is beyond the alcohol, there is somewhere, way beyond what alcohol or drugs give you, it's more blissful than you could possibly imagine, and it's a place that you haven't ventured to yet."

The woman stands still frozen in time, like a rabbit caught in the headlights.

"I know you are scared. We are all scared. But trust me the real you is magnificent. It's not difficult. Find your want and your will and just do it."

The woman half smiles as Scarlet's tone becomes more serious.

"I'm not going to let you drink, if you listen and do the things that are given to you during this flight you will understand differently. You will have the ability to stop. Whatever you are living, however bad it is, take yourself, go into your mind and question, write your answers and you will find a way out."

As the woman turns there is only one thought in her head.

"I really want a drink. No I really need a drink, give me a drink, now."

# CHAPTER 5

# Through the eyes of a child

The child bangs on the table as his father, a middle-aged man darts him a glaring look. The mother who is slightly younger than the father takes the child's hand and holds it still, reassuring the child that it's ok but with a desperate desire in her eyes telling her to stop what she is doing.

The young girl looks up with a look of a typical five-year-old that says, 'Ok, I will stop for a minute, but when you turn back I will do it again.' The mother lets go tending to the slightly older boy of a quieter disposition who is staring out of the window.

"Here, wipe your nose."

The young boy takes the tissue and swipes his nose missing half of its contents, as it spreads across his face.

"Wipe it properly," his mother's voice echoes in his ear.

He wipes again this time taking his attention from the window to the job at hand.

The father is sitting, watching, observing what is taking place in the aircraft, as the uneasiness and fidgeting increases. The boredom of the passengers who have nothing to do, as the edginess and anxiety spreads through the cabin like a disease, each person fuelling the others' energy of agitated aggression.

"This flight is going to be horrific!" He is half talking to himself and half to his wife, who is desperately trying to keep the young girl occupied.

The young girl is standing peering through the gap in the seats to the young couple seated behind them. She slowly edges her hand through the gap between the seats, the minute they see it she withdraws hiding behind the seat, giggling to herself.

"Turn around and sit down."

The young girl continues, oblivious to her mother's pleas. A hand grabs her wrist; her eyes meet her mother's glare.

"Now, sit down."

She turns and sits down, swinging her legs in rhythm with her mischievous mood.

"Now, just sit still otherwise we won't go and see the polar bears."

The young boy looks at his sister.

"Mum. Can I go to the toilet please?"

"Jeremy can you take Frederick to the toilet."

The middle-aged man's attention is fixated on the cabin, the cabin of chaos, children screaming, exasperated parents, irritated adults, angry businessmen and bored teenagers all performing in perfect unison with the accompaniment of impatient fingers tapping on tables, as his wife's soprano voice echoes above it all, as only she can.

"Jeremy! He needs to go to the toilet." She takes the little girl's hand and holds it. "This is absurd, if you see the air stewardess tell her we need the laptops, surely the children can have their laptops."

The man exits from his seat and makes his way up the aisle with his son in front, leading the way as he reaches out touching the petals with his fingertips.

"Dad, why are there flowers on the plane?"

The man pauses for a moment before he answers as he tries to think of something logical to say. "I guess they just want the plane to smell nice."

"Won't they die when we get to Alaska?"

"They will be dead long before that."

"They look nice." The young boy pauses.

"Come on keep going." He gestures for his son to continue to the toilet.

Scarlet makes her way through the cabin observing the world without distraction. To these people, it is as if their world has died. The intense sound of frustrated voices, their minds having no focus, no constant stream of information being fed to them by technology, nothing to tell them what to think, their minds are searching in overdrive as the pressure builds like a pressure cooker ready to explode.

Scarlet's hand reaches for the intercom.

"Ladies and gentlemen, if you could please raise your hands if you are travelling with any children between the ages of three and twelve."

The cabin is silent as parents glance at each other; a look of fear consumes them, desperate to quieten their children, but at the same time slightly fearful of the situation.

Scarlet presses a buzzer as a high-pitched sound resonates through the cabin; the reaction from the passengers is somewhat like a dog when a whistle blows and his uncontrollable behaviour has been stopped dead.

She watches as the passengers perform the perfect stage show. All focused so intently on playing their part, getting it right, behaving how they feel they should behave or rather how they have been taught to behave.

"Do not worry, I am going to take your children off your hands for a little while so you can get some me time. I will be making my way through the cabin to collect them within the next five minutes. Once the children are settled and happy, I will come through the cabin to serve a light but delicious breakfast."

There is a look of uncertainty with some of the mothers; the fathers have nothing but relief running through their minds. Some of the passengers who don't have children express their distain at having to wait for their promised breakfast.

Scarlet wanders through the aircraft and begins to wave upward, making eye contact with all the children. "Can I have all the children stand up please, we are going on an adventure!"

Concerned parents look onward towards Scarlet. Other parents watch as children start to follow. Molly observes the way in which Scarlet leads them like the pied piper through the streets of Hamlin. Scarlet pauses for a moment.

"Now, if I can have all the little children at the front next to me please."

The children stand nervously on the spot, some pushing to the front, others a little more shy who stand transfixed to the spot, a little nervous about leaving their parents, some hugging their favourite toys, others giggling and quibbling. The children eventually make a line, the smaller ones at the front.

"We are going on a BIG adventure, we are going on a special type of adventure called a Mind Sky adventure."

The children look at each other intrigued, their eyes full of wonder.

"Toot Toot! Make way for the magical train travelling through the Mind Flight plane!" Scarlet chants at the top of her voice.

The children giggle.

"Now I want you all to hold hands and sing with me after three, ready. One, two, three. Toot toot! Make way for the magical train travelling through the Mind Flight plane." Scarlet sings as the children follow intermittently, some mimicking not knowing the words, others embarrassed by the intense stares from the audience seated either side of them, some smiling, some completely intent on not paying attention to the raucous behaviour.

A large blue curtain greets them. Scarlet pauses for a second as she turns to face the children. She studies them silently as they stand looking up at her. There are two older children, a boy and a girl, eight children between the ages of six and eleven and one smaller child aged around five.

"Now, we are going to make our way into the outside world but we have to be very quiet passing through the curtain."

The children are silent, with the exception of one little boy who shouts, "Where are the dinosaurs?"

The other children giggle as Scarlet turns, holding her forefinger to her mouth her eyes wide with excitement as she whispers an exaggerated, "Shhh!!"

She opens the curtain, the galley is in darkness, the children pause.

"It's ok, there is nothing to be afraid of, it is only in the darkness that you see the magic, like space when you look up at the sky at night what do you see?"

"Stars!" a young boy's voice shouts out.

"That's right you see stars, thousands of them. They light up the sky and what do we do?"

There is a long pause of silent anticipation.

"We make wishes on them. They are magic stars, so there is nothing to be afraid of when we go into the dark we will see the light, we just have to close our eyes and make a wish and our minds will answer us, if we go into our minds every day we will see the light in whatever we do. Would you like me to go first?" Scarlet asks in a mimicked tone of bravado.

The children nod.

Scarlet makes her way through the curtain as the

children follow. A beautiful pale blue light in the shape of a star lights up the cabin ceiling; as each one passes through it's as if the room is being lit by the most vibrant dots of white light. As the last boy enters the cabin ceiling turns gradually from opaque to transparent to reveal a beautiful star-filled sky.

The children look up in awe their fear replaced by smiles.

"Are we in space?" a little boy announces.

"We are in a special spaceship."

"We have been on a train and now a spaceship." A young girl states with overflowing excitement.

Scarlet reaches into a cupboard and pulls out a bag, she takes out miniature torches and hands them out to the children.

"Now you all have your special light to help you see in the dark, if you can all turn them on please."

The children fumble to press the buttons as the lights illuminate the cabin. Scarlet assists the smaller children as they are greeted by a selection of small pale blue leather chairs with their names on them.

"Wow! Look our names are on the chairs."

"Are there dinosaurs?" the little boy repeats.

"No, there are no dinosaurs in space," another child replies.

"I want to see the dinosaurs."

"You will see a very special dinosaur, the best dinosaur you have ever seen," Scarlet assures the little boy as his eyes widen to double the size. "Now my brave crew I would like you to make your way to your chairs for take off please."

The children make their way at double their normal speed. Scarlet takes the smaller children and sits them next to her. The children sit waiting, some wriggling and fidgeting whilst others remain still and silent.

"Ok, I want everybody to be very quiet we are all going to sit as quietly as we can, until I raise my hand. Okay can you all do that for me?"

The silence is interrupted momentarily as a little voice whispers… "When are we going to see the dinosaurs?"

Scarlet raises her hand and the children become animated.

"Now the reason I asked you to be quiet is because we have a special time that we have when we need to think, this is what we call flying time, when we have flying time we can see and hear all the things that we don't normally see and hear."

The children sit their bodies fidgeting.

"Now I want you to be still like statues, not a movement."

Scarlet follows with a dramatically long pause.

"Now close your eyes."

She looks at the young boy twisting and turning, she leans over placing her hand on his lap, helping him to close his eyes. The youngest boy sits eyes wide-open.

"If you want to see the dinosaur you have to behave like one. What do dinosaurs do when they are hiding in the forest?"

The young boy looks at her as his eyes search for the answer.

"Still. They are still." Another child shouts out.

"That's right, dinosaurs stay very still when they are hiding in the forest. If you stay very very still you might see one."

The little boy gradually morphs into a statue as everyone else follows suit.

She leaves them for a minute as they sit concealing their excitement in the mask of silence.

"Can anybody tell me what you heard when you were in your flying time?"

Frederick an eight-year-old child raises his hand.

"I heard the rumble of the engines and some people were coughing. I also heard some things jostle and move about."

"We hear things in the darkness very clearly, just like we see things in the darkness we become like super heroes with x-ray vision and x-ray hearing, we become strong."

She turns to another child of about eight as she waits for him to answer. He remains silent, Scarlet smiles reassuringly as she takes her attention to an eleven-year-old girl.

"It's Amberley, isn't it?" Amberley's face beams with joy that Scarlet knows her name.

"I managed to make sense of the sounds around me, some talking in the back and then they seemed to drift away and I thought I heard my…" Amberley pauses.

Scarlet notices a small tear trickle down Amberley's face.

"Tell me?"

"We are moving to Alaska, as my father no longer wants to work in the city."

Amberley pauses for a moment.

Scarlet smiles, nodding as she takes her focus to another child, as Amberley continues.

"My mum died."

Scarlet pauses for a second.

"I want to see the dinosaurs. I'm Spiderman!" Scarlet glances down at the little boy next to her as she picks him up, sitting him on her lap, as he holds his hands out towards her making a whooshing sound.

"What was that?" Scarlet asks.

"It's my web. I'm Spiderman." The children chuckle.

"What did Liam hear when we were being very quiet?"

"My owl."

"Your owl?"

"There he is!" he points out in front of him. The other children begin to giggle. Liam gets even more excited. "There he is." The other children laugh. "There!" He points in a different direction, and again as he giggles hysterically at the recognition of his comic genius.

"Can you tell us all about your owl friend?"

"He can fly. I saw him fly."

"Listening is very important, not only listening to others, but also listening to the quietness and being calm, because you hear the things that you wouldn't normally hear. Listening to the world around us is one of the most important things we can do when we become adults."

Scarlet's words are interrupted.

"My dad says my mum never listens," a young boy informs the crowd.

Scarlet smiles. "Well you will have to teach your mum to have some 'flying time,' and she will begin to listen more."

She takes her attention back to Amberley as she holds her gaze.

"Amberley. Whatever happens you know that your mother is still with us. The fact that she has left the physical world simply means that she is living in your heart. We keep our loved ones alive by celebration, not by sorrow. Your mother is with you, she is there always, making sure you are safe, guiding you."

Amberley smiles, slightly embarrassed, but her face reflects some sense of comfort.

"When you think of her, allow the light of her memory, her smile, her hug, her kisses to shine through you and she will give you strength.

"You are starting a new adventure it's not frightening, it's exciting. The best thing you can do is embrace it. In life there will always be both good and bad, but remember to embrace both as they will help you to understand more.

"Don't try to fight or run away from the bad times because you will waste precious lifetime, they will always exist, you will never be able to escape the bad times but you can learn to understand the lesson it is teaching you, and in understanding you will become stronger, and it won't hurt you in the same way.

"Focus on understanding it so you can let it go. Once you have experienced it, it becomes the past, it has been lived, like a non-stop train speeding past you at a station. It is there in an instance and then it is gone, vanishing into the distance, never to be seen again."

"I'm going on a trip to Alaska so that I can see all the wildlife," says Fredrick. "When we get there we are going on a train and a plane, one that goes on water and we're going to fly it around the mountains."

"I asked Owl, and I am going to fly on Owl's back and he is going to take me everywhere, up in the sky and down and up in the sky! He is going to take me to see the bears." Frederick and the others chuckled.

Scarlet reaches upwards into the ceiling and pulls down a large flexible screen, a loud gasp follows. She flicks a switch on the screen and it suddenly lights up, all that can be seen are white fluffy clouds.

"Liam what do you see?"

"Marshmallows!"

The other children join in as a chorus of voices follows.

"It looks like a giant white cloud and I can see so many animals in the clouds."

"Look you can see an elephant and an owl and a tiger. There! There! Look a dinosaur!" Liam points mesmerized.

"I want to go outside and see him?"

"Sometimes we can only see things from a distance, we feel them but we cannot touch them, but they are as real as anything we have ever known."

"Wow! You can actually look outside this plane, we are looking outside right now. I can see the wing and an engine. This is so cool; we are looking at ourselves it's like we are standing outside." Frederick is up out of his seat as he runs towards the window; his face appears on the screen. The children giggle.

"We have a special camera that allows us to look at ourselves, it's like when we look into a mirror, we see everything. It is important to look at things from a different place as we sometimes forget who we are, it is always good to remember to look at who we are from outside ourselves."

"The only way you see that this plane can fly is because it has wings that stretch out either side, so the air may flow beneath it. The engines make the wind beneath the wings flow faster and faster, which means we can go higher and higher.

"You see this is how we can stay up in the air. We can't see the air but we can feel it and if you feel enough of it the air can become as strong as steel and as light as nothing itself, we can breathe it. It keeps us all alive, because breath for all of us is life."

Then in a sudden moment of realization Frederick shouts out, "Wow! The plane is flying because it is breathing."

"That's right, if we don't breathe the air into our own engines then we can no longer fly and if we breathe new air into our engines everyday we fly more powerfully stronger and for longer."

Liam wriggles restlessly. "I'm going to teach Owl to breath so he can fly really, really far and I can be the fastest!"

A fit of hysterical laughter consumes the spaceship, the children giggle unable to contain their excitement.

Scarlet shouts out pulling a funny face. "Pokky nana cubawonga." The children look at her unable to contain their laughter.

She looks to Amberley. "Make up a word, as crazy a word as you can, let your imagination run wild." Amberley looks a little embarrassed. "Go on I know there is a crazy word in you."

Amberley giggles coyly drawing her neck to her chin in an attempt to hide as she suddenly bursts out with the word. "Tonga tanka ti ti."

The children roar with laughter. Amberley cannot stop giggling.

"Chubby chukka chi chi, Ponty pokanana, Omchuck."

"Owl! Owl Owl! Owl! Owl," Liam continues not knowing when to stop as the children laugh louder, he gets louder.

Scarlet reaches into the galley area taking out a little white bag. She pauses waiting for the laughter to quieten down.

"I have a little gift for all of you, always keep them near you. They will help you to remember our little talk and when you look at them it is like looking at the Mind Flight plane on the screen here, you will remember what the plane does to stay up in the air... how many of you will remember?" She pulls a quizzical face. The children begin to giggle. She pulls an even bigger quizzical face. "I don't think you can remember?" she states louder in a more questioning tone.

A chorus of high-pitched excitable voices answers her as the children shout.

"He breathes!"

"You do remember!!"

Amberley interjects. "When we feel scared we close our eyes, go into the darkness, and we breathe."

Scarlet ceremoniously hands out the white fluffy Mind Flight planes to each of the children.

"Wow! They are so detailed and all the windows are blue."

"Look! It has Mind Flight written on it."

Frederick began by moving the plane through the air, flying it up and around as Liam sat hugging his plane.

"All journeys have to come to an end. Take with you what you have learnt on any journey so that you may use that knowledge whenever you need to. Remember the good and learn from the bad, there are no mistakes in life they are just learning curves. Every part of life's journey is beautiful, when you see the beauty in it all, then life is lived in every breath."

Scarlet is lost in the moment, in the moment of sharing she pauses for a moment reminding herself why children are such an inspiration.

"Can I show my mummy and daddy and my baby sister?" Before Scarlet has time to answer Liam was up and off, crawling under the curtain as he ran back to his parents.

Scarlet opens the curtains letting the children run back to their seats; she turns and presses a button so the screen retracts.

Amberley stands behind her waiting. "Thank you so much."

Scarlet turns to meet Amberley's hands clasping the plane tightly.

"I'm going to use this so much to remind me of today. I know that as long as I have this plane with me, that my life is a journey of new experiences."

Scarlet nods in acknowledgement.

"I'm going to learn from this journey with my mother. I can use this plane. I can always fly towards the comforting memories of my mother and of the adventure to come. I can fly in my imagination to safety."

Scarlet reaches out, hugging her as she speaks.

"This is your plane and you may fly wherever or whenever you wish. This plane will take you to your dreams and comfort you when you sleep. It will fly you through fear and the unknown. It can fly you towards the answers whenever you have questions.

"Whenever you need to fly, just look at this plane and it will take you to where your heart and your mind desires, and then your spirit will soar."

The moment is interrupted by Frederick's hand as he reaches out to shake Scarlet's hand. Scarlet returns the gesture with a warm caring hug. The children look proud of themselves all standing a little straighter and more confident.

After a while all that could be heard was the gentle synchronicity of quiet snores as the excitement and the experience left them in a gentle state of sleepy wonder.

# CHAPTER 6

# Nothing matters. Only now matters.

Jake sits looking at the table in front of him not sure whether to laugh or cry. He glances to Molly who is deep in thought staring at the vast landscape that greets her out of the aircraft window.

"I really don't like this," Jake states with an air of seriousness.

Molly looks to him, her manner is calm and collected. "Why?"

"I don't know, it just doesn't feel right."

"In what way?"

"I don't know it just feels strange, nothing is normal. I feel strange."

Molly smiles a sympathetic smile. Somewhere deep down inside of her in that place that no one else can reach but her she feels the same. She knows that it isn't a bad feeling, but it's an odd feeling, a feeling that she hasn't felt before. For a moment she tries to think about what the feeling is, but she can't put her finger on it. It's not a scared feeling, it's not anger, and it's not fear, maybe uncertainty. Maybe it's the feeling of uncertainty, the feeling of the unknown.

It feels as though everything up to this point in her life she has never examined. She has never taken the time to look at her life, trying to be a success at what she does, trying to make money to sustain the normal lifestyle of working then holiday, then working then Christmas. Then it all begins again with a New Year's resolution which lasts for about a month at the most and then it's back on the same old treadmill.

She realizes that this is her life and right now, it's stopped. Everything she has known to this point has stopped. There are no distractions, just the sky, the silence and the thoughts in her head.

She reassures herself this isn't normal, so it's bound to feel uncertain. Her mind flips into uncertainty, sitting with just her thoughts in an alien environment. It is unknown because right now we have no idea what the next hour will bring.

She turns to Jake.

"I know why we feel like this."

He looks at her.

"It's uncertainty."

He looks away in despair.

"That's ok. It is uncertain we don't know what's going to happen in the next hour as we are not in control, that's why we feel strange."

The intercom clicks as Scarlet's in breath is caught in the air moments before she commences her speech.

"I would like you all to take out the safety card in the seat pocket in front of you and refer to point five on the back of the card."

Molly takes out the card.

"Don't die before you have lived, don't live before you have died."

Jake glances to Molly a look of fear consumes them as Scarlet's words invade the moment.

"When you understand this statement, then you will truly live, that is your challenge on this flight. To reach that understanding. If you manage to understand then from the moment you depart from this aircraft you will truly live your life as it is supposed to be lived.

"In the here, in the now, in the present moment. Then you will no longer feel uncertain and nothing will feel unknown. When you are focused on the present you will move forward in life, as your energy will be directed exactly where it is supposed to be.

"And now to live completely in the present moment – it's time for food! I will be making my way through the cabin if there is anything you don't like please let me know and I will do my best to accommodate."

The intercom clicks.

Molly studies the safety card; she plays the last few words over in her head.

"You know they are right, the only certainty we do have in life is death."

Jake looks at her with a look of resigned fear.

"I just want us to land."

"No, seriously. If you were going to die today what would you do?"

"Now is the worst possible time you could say something like that to me."

"I'm not joking. What would you do?" she asks.

"Well there aren't many options up here are there?"

Molly sits thinking; she isn't listening to what Jake is saying. She is thinking about what she would do if this were her last day. She glances at Jake and has a moment of realization as Scarlet reaches out holding a tablecloth. Molly is taken out of the moment, as she opens her table. As she pulls it down she notices the table is engraved in simple blue writing. 'Nothing matters, only now matters.' She looks to Jake's table as he pulls it down with an urgency of having something that is normal for a little while. The same words stare back up at him.

"Nothing matters, only now matters," he smiles at Molly.

"Now that is true."

Scarlet holds out the tablecloth, Jake hesitates not sure what to do with it.

"If you would like to place it over the table it will make the whole experience much more pleasurable," Scarlet instructs.

Jake lays the cloth over his table. He glances around to see who is looking at him, his eyes are met by a cabin of people, heads down, silent, devouring the food in front of them, he takes his attention to the portly man who is sound asleep and the young fifteen year old boy across the aisle whose mother is feeding him. His hands rest in his lap as he closes his mouth his mother wipes it with her cloth.

"I love this food Mum. Why can't you make food like this?"

Jake stares at the mother as she continues feeding him. There is a tiredness in her eyes. A tiredness that reveals the life she leads, a life of looking after the one thing that is most precious to her in the entire world, her son. The young boy notices Jake staring.

"Don't you like the food?"

Jake pauses for a moment a little embarrassed.

"No! Yes!"

"I love it. It's so delicious, it's better than first class."

He looks at the young boy's first class food. The food is beautifully presented, the cosiness of the cutlery finely wrapped in cotton napkins. The exquisite bottled water, the doughnut that looks as though it has been hand made and freshly baked moments before. The backdrop icing the colour of the sky as a white plane ascends up into the sky, like a rocket taking off with the words 'Devour and Delight' trailing from its contrails. To finish it off quotes of comfort and love are sprinkled across each item on the tray.

The young boy points his hands to the napkin that gently surrounds the doughnut.

"This is my favourite one… Goodness is gratefulness!"

He looks to his mother with a look of urgency. His mother picks the doughnut up leading it to his mouth as he leans into his delight, sinking his teeth into it.

Jake smiles as he takes his attention back to his own food, pausing for a moment. This isn't like his normal journeys, his business trips in first class where he doesn't even stop to eat food, let alone watch others eat it. His trips are always consumed by his endless amounts of work; he sits staring at the spectacle in front of him. The passengers are actually enjoying the food, for a moment his strange feeling dissipates as he is focused on what his stomach is telling him, he realizes he's famished.

His eyes meet a silver tray. A tall pale blue frosted glass bottle with a contemporary white aircraft engraved onto the side of the bottle with the words 'Empower and Elevate' trailing in the wake of the aircraft's engraved contrails stands greeting him.

He has an urgency to taste the water. He reaches out lifting the bottle and as he looks down his eyes are awoken by the lid of the bottle. 'Water is life on Earth' circles the exterior of the bottle cap. Like a halo circling the earth. He turns the bottle around 'A secret source of purity from the snow-capped mountains of the north'. He pauses for a moment before looking to Molly.

She looks at him.

"I like this."

# CHAPTER 7

# How can you be a sceptic when you don't know what's going on?

Molly watches as the sun begins to prepare for rest; the sky changes from the vibrancy of a white light shining on the ocean to the haziness of a boat searching for land in fog as the Earth turns away from the only source of light available for trillions of miles. A time when dreaming begins as the mind turns to the eyes of the imagination revealing what our real eyes fail to see, bringing forth a state of sleep and dream.

It's a time to set off on an expedition to see, not the world around us but a world as seen by our thinking eyes.

Molly has sat looking at her notepad for the past two hours waiting for that moment of inspiration, that trigger of creativity. All she has done is think, think about the questions that are staring back at her from her notepad. What is her story? More thoughts follow... What is her film? What is good about it? What is lacking in it? Surely, she must know by now.

She knows she is living and doing something. She makes money, but is that her real purpose? The life that is happening around her right now is a world that she hasn't experienced before, the strangeness of not having her belongings, the distractions of watching a movie or listening to music. All she is left with are the thoughts in her head and right now it feels as though her entire life makes no sense whatsoever.

All she knows is that she has the past flipping into her head like a yoyo, each time it reaches her hand before she can grasp it, it is back flying to the floor again.

All the things she has ever experienced, all the joys and the pains are giving her a grand performance. A performance that is making her feel uncomfortable, so uncomfortable that she wants to run away and hide in a corner and never surface again.

She watches Scarlet hurry along the aisle, for a moment she thinks about the stewardess's life. Waiting on people, flying up in the sky everyday, never knowing where you will be from one week to the next, like a spirit flying through life. For a moment she can see the appeal as she watches Scarlet smiling at the man who has called for her attention.

"May I have a glass of wine please?"

"I'm sorry sir we don't have any wine on the Mind Flight plane."

"Can I have a glass of champagne then please?"

"I'm sorry sir. We have no alcohol aboard the aircraft."

"Then why have I paid for a first class seat if there is no alcohol?"

"There isn't first class on the aircraft sir, it is all one class."

The gentleman sports a black leather jacket and has a face that resembles an aged politician. He looks at the people around him, they are all sitting in large seats, tulips are scattered in all the seat pockets and the infamous tags of knowledge hang waiting, waiting to grab the attention of the person seated in front of them.

"This looks like first class to me."

"The entire aircraft is like this sir."

"Then why have I paid for a first class seat, if it isn't first class?"

His wife interrupts. "We didn't pay." He doesn't answer. "It was a gift." The gentleman looks bemused. "A gift from my mother. I knew if I told you that you wouldn't accept it."

"We should still have drink whether she paid or not."

"Trust me sir by the end of the flight you will not require alcohol to fly."

The middle-aged woman next to him starts to fidget and cough nervously. Scarlet notices her hands are shaking.

"I do not need alcohol to fly. I want it."

"Trust me sir by the end of the flight you will not want it."

"With all due respect madam. I know what I want and what I don't want."

"Is there anything—" Her sentence is cut short as the man raises his hand indicating a forceful stop.

"Before you start all this mumbo jumbo of telling me

to breathe and calm down, I don't want to know. Who really wants to spend their time sitting breathing, what a waste of time?"

"Sir, I completely understand where you are coming from but may I ask you to consider a couple of things.

"Firstly, how can you be a sceptic when you have no idea what's going on? And secondly, I would ask you to think about your last statement about breathing, really think about it – breath is life, without it you don't have one."

She smiles.

"Now sir is there anything else I can get for you?"

"No. There is nothing I want other than my first request for a drink."

Scarlet takes her attention from the man to his partner.

"Madam, would you like a drink?"

She glances to her husband as she smiles. Silently nodding an uncertain 'No'.

"What is this all about? Is it some kind of religion or cult?" the man asks.

"No sir. Our belief is simple. Our belief is unconditional love."

"I love my wine, so if you are serving love then surely you are obligated to make it available."

"I'm sorry sir love is very different to unconditional love. And we only serve the unconditional kind."

CHAPTER 8

# Depressions are there to guide us

The cabin lights dim as they gradually fade to darkness; the intercom clicks as everyone awaits the announcement in anticipation.

The vastness of the stars prepare to show themselves formed by the unequalled talent of nature itself, the largest most eloquent canvas, the darkness of space brings a new light deep within the recesses of the cosmos. The greatest discoveries in life are made in the midst of darkness; this is where the light of day shows itself more truthful in our lives than ever before.

"Good evening ladies and gentlemen. As you can see we have dimmed the cabin lights to complete darkness, there will be no light for the next fifteen minutes. If you need to use the bathroom please do so now by pushing the button on the left hand side of your seat at which point a red light will light up above your seat. If you see a red light light up near you can you please push your own light button to light the way for the other passenger."

"Wouldn't it just be easier to put all the lights back on so we are safe?" a male voice resounds in the darkness.

The intercom clicks. "Yes, it most definitely would sir. However, I would much prefer for you to pay attention to each other's needs and assist in keeping each other safe."

Silence consumes the cabin. The intercom clicks.

"Ok, so no one would like to use the bathroom?"

A silent cabin responds.

"I would like you all to close your eyes and focus on the centre of your forehead. Focus on that black screen inside your forehead; every time a thought comes in I want you to repeat silently: I am now focused on my mind and nothing will interfere."

Scarlet silently makes her way through the cabin stopping at every seat, she reaches out and gently places her finger in the centre of each persons forehead, holding for a few seconds. She is greeted by people sitting with their eyes open, some sleep, some staring into the darkness, others who are obeying her instructions and are on their own journey into the darkness of their minds.

A child begins to cry uncontrollably as the mother panics. Scarlet makes her way to the child.

"I'm sorry he is afraid of the dark, he hates the dark. I hated the dark as a child."

Scarlet places her hands gently onto his head and the child begins to calm, she crouches down taking his hand.

"Have you heard the story about the dark?"

The little boy shakes his head too scared to speak.

"Ok, if you promise you won't be scared. When I go

away I will tell you a story. A very special story on my loudspeaker just for you."

She gently rubs his head as the little boy's tears lessen momentarily.

Scarlet makes her way back, the intercom clicks.

"Ladies and gentlemen we have a little boy on board who is scared of the dark. I am going to tell him a story so please bear with me." Her voice echoes in the darkness, his crying the backdrop to the story.

"There was once a little boy and girl who were scared of the dark. As soon as the lights went out at night, they became fearful and scared because they couldn't see anything and they had no idea what or who was out there.

"One evening when they were both crying the little boy felt something gently touch his head and he suddenly stopped crying, no matter how hard he tried he just couldn't cry. When he stopped crying the little girl saw him stop and she stopped too.

"She said to the little boy, 'Why did you stop crying?'

"The little boy thought for a minute before replying, 'I don't know, I just didn't feel scared anymore.'

"The little girl began to cry, again. But the little boy remained calm as he reached out and put his hands on her head, the little girl gradually began to stop crying, she looked at the little boy and she said, 'I don't feel scared anymore, look it's dark and I'm not scared.'

"They both started giggling. 'But why don't we feel scared?'

"The little boy had no answers, he tried to think but

he couldn't. He was so focused on finding the answer to his question that he didn't feel scared at all. Then suddenly he heard a voice in the darkness telling him to close his eyes and to ask the question silently to his mind. He closed his eyes and whispered to his mind. 'Why do we not feel scared anymore?'

"'Because there is nothing to fear. It is in the darkness when you close your eyes, that you will find all of your answers. I am sitting here in the silence waiting for you to ask, all you need to do is ask and I will have an answer for you. How can the darkness be scary if it has the answer to all of your questions?

"'When you are in the dark and you get scared it's just my little friends, the emotions, they will want to play as they love playing games. They love having fun, if they start talking to you and making you feel scared then just close your eyes and ask me to tell them to stop playing around and scaring you and I will.

"'I am here waiting to teach you whenever you need me. I am here to protect you, to guide you and look after you. But you can only speak to me when you close your eyes and look into the darkness, I live in a magical place where your wishes live, the place where magic happens.'

"The little boy had one final question for his mind. 'Who touched me on the head?'

"'It was me, reminding you that I am here to help you.'"

Scarlet pauses for a moment… the cabin falls silent.

"We all go into the darkness sometimes, we all become

lost. When we reach that level of despair, when there is no way out, our emotions begin to affect our physical being. This is a time when we must ask our minds for help. The darkness is our mind encouraging us to think. We see them as depressions but they are our greatest teacher. It is in these moments that we receive the most, when we ask our minds to guide us, to show us the way. When we open to a higher state of consciousness we begin to see truth, when we see truth we understand, when we understand our fears go away.

"Depressions are there to serve us, to guide us, and to protect us. Embrace the depression; go into the darkness of your mind, question and your answer will be revealed to you.

"Once we accept that light and dark are part of us, life becomes easier. We cannot have day without night, both serve a valuable purpose. When we fear them they consume us, when we embrace them we overcome. When we clear the conscious mind of all restrictions then we allow the subconscious to flow freely, without hindrance.

"When we learn to understand our depressions then we have fulfilled our ultimate objective as human beings.

"It is our duty to keep ourselves well by going into our minds and understanding our depression, when we are living in the world of the dead the only way to bring life is to question. The mind is ready waiting to help you to understand."

Scarlet pauses.

"I would like you all to take a deep breath in through the nose and out through the mouth. When you take the breath, I would like you all to think the words new life, power and strength begin to instruct your mind.

"When we are told to breathe with a thought, with an objective what does the thought do? It sends a message to the mind to obey the instruction, the mind instructs the brain, the brain instructs the body to change.

"I want you to breathe into new life, power and strength. Remember, the deep breath does nothing by itself, but when you make it objective with an instruction and you begin to breathe into the mind you activate everything, you switch everyone on. When you breathe you empower, when you empower you elevate."

Some passengers fidget uncertainly, desperate to try it and intrigued by the mystery. Others listen out of utter boredom, resigned to the fact that they have no choice.

The young man places his hands onto his lap and breathes. He is embracing every moment, every instruction, he is on his journey. He is living in the here and in the now. The middle-aged woman closes her eyes as she attempts to find what lays beyond, for she has no choice but to try.

Molly looks at Jake sitting with his arms crossed, a look of refusal on his face. Molly takes a breath in encouraging him to participate as she does so. He doesn't move from his fixed stare that is looking at the seat back in front of him. She gets more confident, taking another breath and another.

The young boy to her left is breathing, he is focused, and the breath is flowing.

The cabin is silent, save for the feeling of the invisible energy that is encompassing the passengers. The energy that they are unaware of, an energy that is lifting them to a different state of being.

"Breathe like it is your first breath of life. When we are born it is that first breath that brings us life, that explodes and brings our entire being into existence. I want you to breathe like that first breath with all the passion for life that you had when you were released into the world with all the power, strength and possibility for the new life that awaited you, for breath brings life."

The group of people around the young girl are breathing. There are many who are looking out of the window, chatting, staring in front of them pretending that this moment isn't happening, that they are not really sitting on a plane with everyone breathing.

Molly has a thought come into her head, *I am sitting on a plane with 200 other people and I am breathing.* She repeats the thought over again. I am sitting on a plane full of people breathing, but that is exactly what I am doing, for life we need breath and everyone on the plane is breathing. Why do people feel so strange about it? Because that is what they are doing already but all we are doing now is thinking about the breath and paying attention to it. Paying attention to the thing that keeps us alive. Why do we give attention to everything else and yet the thing that sustains us we don't ever think about it?

The intercom clicks.

Captain Dennis takes a breath. "When you are ready

you may come back, you may come back. When you are ready. You may come back. You may come back to life."

A serene energy radiates through the cabin.

Molly opens her eyes, it takes her a moment to adjust to the world that greets her, a world that is different to the world she left a few moments ago, for everything is clear. She stares at the flower in front of her, the white tulip that before was just a lovely tulip but now it is different. The shading, the colour, the detail of the petals the shape of the leaves, the way they are so perfectly formed, it's as if the tulip has come to life. Her world transformed from the grainy undefined world of VHS to the sharp high resolution world of Blu-ray.

She turns her attention to the scene outside of her window: the wing that before was just a wing fighting against the wind in its fragility and fearsomeness has transformed into a wing of power and strength, of magnificent strength for it is guiding us, it is supporting us, it is flying us.

# CHAPTER 9

# Love

Her hand grasps his hand as she snuggles her head into his shoulder. He squeezes, she looks up, she squeezes back, he squeezes harder, she giggles. The portly man in the seat in front of them peers through the gap in the seats shooting a disapproving look.

They both glance out of the window. He turns, sighing.

"Jess look." The young boy gestures to the girl to look down. She leans across him.

"I can't see anything."

He tickles her waist as she starts to giggle.

"Further down there." He points down.

She leans in further.

"There's nothing there," she states with an air of frustration.

"You need to really look and you will see."

She stares out in the darkness her hands cupped around her face.

"I can't see anything." She rubs her eyes.

"You got it."

"What?"

"You saw it."

"What are you talking about?"

"You saw what I saw, there is nothing there, we are free."

She frowns at him. He grabs her head like a rugby player in the midst of a scrum.

"We aren't free we are on a plane with lots of people."

"We are free from reality, normality doesn't exist up here."

She grabs his hand feeling uneasy at the thought. He rubs her head as she smiles sweetly.

He leans into her kissing her gently on the neck. "I'm sorry."

She smiles. She kisses him on the cheek. He kisses her on the lips, she giggles, he tickles, she giggles again, louder this time.

The sound of the flight attendant's buzzer rings. Scarlet makes her way down the cabin as the portly gentlemen seated in front of the teenage couple adjusts his silk polka-dot cravat.

"Can you please sort these two teenagers out behind my seat please? They are giggling and it's very infuriating."

Scarlet glances at the young couple. It's the perfect scene from the perfect movie. Laughter surrounds them, they are alone, they are free and they are loving the moment, they are loving the freedom, they are loving each other, they are laughing. They are alive.

"I'm sorry sir, I really don't feel that I want to destroy something so perfect." He looks at her astounded. "Look at them, they are happy. How many moments do you get in life where you are that happy?"

The man turns as he peers over his tortoiseshell rimmed spectacles as he looks through the gap. The two teenagers catch his gaze, the moment is lost, the laughter is gone for a second. Their faces show no expression, there is nothing on the surface, but as he turns back their faces begin to release as they open their mouths into fits of hysteria. Scarlet cannot help but giggle at the innocence. She glances back at the portly man realizing his frustration.

"Sir, I can move your seat if you would like?"

"I'm not moving. I'm perfectly happy here. Why should I move?"

"Ok sir, I will ask the young couple if they would like to move."

Scarlet makes her way towards the young couple.

"Would you like to move to a more private seat at the back of the aircraft? I have two seats in the corner at the back."

They glance at each other with the same level of excitement as a group of children on Christmas Eve. They unbuckle their seat belts and stand ceremoniously with their belongings in hand, ready to move.

Scarlet smiles and guides them to the back of the aircraft. They can hardly contain their excitement; the smiles she receives are never ending.

The portly man turns looking at the two empty seats behind him. Smiling, he glances to the gentleman in the seat next to him, a Middle Eastern gentleman dressed in full headdress. The gentleman smiles at him.

The portly man feels compelled to speak.

"That's better isn't it?"

The gentleman speaks in a slow powerful manner. A strong Middle Eastern accent envelops every word.

"Do you know that the heart is the first thing to form when we are conceived?" The portly man is not sure how to react. "At twenty-one days it starts to form," he pauses. "Do you know that the heart is the very last thing to stop when we die?"

The portly man is surprised at the fact.

"The heart is the ruler."

"That's all very romantic—"

"It's fact. I am a cardiac surgeon."

The portly man is silenced as he nods nervously.

Scarlet reaches out to the young couple who are transfixed watching the sky as it evolves from day to night.

"Would you like a blanket and pillow?"

She holds out two pale blue cashmere blankets with 'Mind Flight' delicately engraved in silk on each corner.

The young girl takes the blanket rubbing it against her cheek. Scarlet hands her a pale blue silk pillow, with 'Sleep is your friend', engraved on the corner.

"What are your names?" Scarlet asks.

Jessica looks to the young man to take the lead.

"Jessica and Andy."

Scarlet smiles "They are beautiful names. Sleep tight." She turns, walking away.

"I love these, I love them so much," Jessica hugs the pillow.

"I love you," he leans in and whispers into her ear.

"I told you we are free."

CHAPTER 10

# Looking in the mirror

Molly waits patiently as the access light turns from red to green – the door opens. The cabin is in darkness. A dark-haired man in his thirties, with a face that could have belonged to Cary Grant exits holding the door for her.

"Thank you." She smiles.

He holds her gaze a little longer than would normally be appropriate. She looks away.

She closes the door, puts the cover on the toilet seat down before she carefully balances over the toilet, desperate not to let any part of her body touch the seat. The daunting vacuous sound of the toilet whirs away beneath her, as she is lost in her thoughts.

Her thoughts about the journey so far, her thoughts about her life, her relationship with Jake. Something she hasn't thought about for a long time, her daily life is a mix of meetings, friends, the gym and walking on the weekend. But where is her life going? Why are her and Jake together? Who is she? Is she a good person to be questioning if Jake and her should be together after all of this time? What is the story that she will leave behind?

She stands staring in the mirror, tears trickle down her cheeks. Her thoughts are interrupted by a banging on the door.

She pushes the buttons on the hand wash trying not to touch anything else in the vicinity of the basin. She washes and dries, glances at herself in the mirror at the bags beneath her eyes. She looks at herself; the look becomes a prolonged stare.

She wipes the mascara from beneath her eyes bringing herself back to reality, remembering there is someone outside waiting. She flicks her hair, straightens her back and turns the lock on the door to exit.

She opens the door and he is there again, the man who she met on her entrance, the man who held her gaze for a little longer than appropriate.

"I'm sorry for knocking. I think I may have left my watch on the sink."

Molly smiles.

"You get a little lost up here."

He smiles.

"Or maybe you are found." He states in a matter of fact manner.

She smiles, making a quick exit as she walks down the aisle to her seat.

The aircraft is silent and still, there are no lights from the TVs, laptops or phones, there is no activity.

Molly notices a couple who are sitting to the left, an

elderly couple, immaculately dressed in fact, they are sitting holding hands, the gentleman asleep on her shoulder as she gazes out of the window.

For a second Molly wonders what their story is? What trials have they overcome in life? And what has brought them to this point, together now on this journey? She thinks about her and Jake how they will be when they get to that age, she glances down the cabin to where they are seated. She can see Jake's head, the only person on the plane with the blanket practically suffocating him, hidden from this intriguing yet unusual world.

The aircraft drops hitting an air pocket as she holds onto the seat to the right of her, the empty seat, she steadies herself as she looks down. There is the white notepad open on the seat, the title that has been staring up at her for the past five hours, the questions that she has been too scared to answer.

She glances back to the pad, the page is full of writing, the first line, 'I know who I am. I know what I want.' The plane interrupts again with a shudder but she continues to read, holding on. 'I want real, I want unconditional. I want truth.'

The seat belt sign beeps a warning that it is time to go, she cannot take her eyes off the page, 'I want unconditional. Love. I want an unconditional life.'

The red seatbelt sign lights up as a hand touches her shoulder.

"Excuse me, may I get to my seat."

Molly turns her head ever so slightly, in an

embarrassed I've have been caught type of way. She turns again smiling.

"I'm sorry the turbulence, I just paused for a second."

"I know. I was behind you."

This time the aircraft makes the decision for her as it jolts from left to right as Scarlet's voice is heard over the loudspeaker.

"Ladies and gentlemen, please return to your seats. We are about to hit a little turbulence, if you could please return to your seats immediately and fasten your seatbelts."

Molly turns to the dark-haired man behind her. The man whose hand is still resting on her shoulder using it as an armrest to steady himself.

"I had better go," Molly mutters under her breath.

He smiles, removing his hand.

Molly makes an exit as she makes her way down the cabin. Scarlet meets her walking in the opposite direction.

"Are you ok?" Scarlet asks in her gentle reassuring manner.

Molly acknowledges with a subtle nod.

"Don't worry if the lights go out you will find your way home. It is only in the darkness that we find our destiny." Scarlet interrupts her thoughts, pointing to the ground. "The lights. They will lead you back to your seat."

Molly smiles and heads back. She doesn't notice anyone else on the way, just a sea of heads all facing forwards, her only focus is on the empty seat next to Jake. She reaches her seat and quietly sits down. Jake stirs, as the blanket falls to the floor, she slowly lifts it back up so not to disturb him. He turns groaning.

She fastens her seatbelt and takes her attention outside, to the wing of the aircraft, to the fragility and the fearsomeness of it. The fragility in the way it bends and the fearsomeness as it battles against the air that is tempting it, that is pressuring it to fall. She looks back to the book in front of her, the book with the blank page. Jake stirs as he opens his eyes, she glances back out of the window.

"Look at the sky over there, it's so dark." Molly points to the black clouds that beckon to the right.

Jake is sitting upright, rummaging through the seat pocket in front of him.

"All the money they have spent on all this, they could have at least given us earplugs. How much did this set us back?"

Molly looks at Jake. Jake looks away exasperated.

"They were free," Molly reveals.

"What do you mean they were free?"

"They were free, I was given them, we were chosen."

"REALLY!" Jake looks at her with a look that says only you could do something like that.

"I thought it would be a nice surprise."

"Good Morning," there is a long pause.

"Oh here we go again!" Molly nudges Jake commanding his silence.

Jake reclines his chair and closes his eyes.

Scarlet continues "Write until your mind clears. Thoughts that just sit in your head tire you out and take you down. Thoughts and emotions will surface, thoughts from the past. It is important to eliminate these thoughts by seeing them, understanding them and letting them go. When you rid yourself of these thoughts you will have space to think, to fill your mind with more constructive objective thoughts. When you become aware of who you are and how you work you will have an awareness of what is real and what isn't, but more importantly what is restricting you. When you detach from your emotions you see things clearly from a different perspective, your decisions are made from a place of calmness and clarity."

Jake pulls his blanket over his head. Molly aimlessly gazes out of the window into a void of darkness. She turns back to her notepad looking at the words staring back at her. The blank page that can relieve all of her past and all of her pain and yet she chooses to take her attention to her surroundings.

# CHAPTER 11

# Facing your truth

Molly scans the cabin and she meets the eyes of the young man, who is staring at her. He is in his thirties, he is of slim build and has a nature that is somewhat like a snail. He stands looking around the aircraft as if he were conserving energy to make the most important announcement. Standing long enough to draw the attention of everyone in his vicinity, but at the last minute deciding not to speak.

She watches as he proceeds to make his way down the aisle, smiling and nodding at everyone as he passes saying good morning. The passengers glance up at him not sure whether to smile or hide, smiles that attempt to conceal their fear.

He pauses half way along the aisle, he has spotted the person who has connected with him.

"Hi, how you doing?"

The person who has connected with him is the old lady, who sits holding hands with the elderly gentleman seated next to her. The old couple who Molly was intrigued by, who look like they have stepped out of a 1940's movie.

"Yes, thank you! I'm very well young man."

"I must say your energy attracted me to you, I can feel people's energy."

"I have to say it was your good looks that caught my eye. I haven't had anyone your age look at me for years."

"We are all connected, my guru tells me that we are all connected. I'm a good person you know, I have great integrity and I help people, I am always helping people, I'm on a mission to save the planet."

The old lady studies him before she speaks. "I can't say that I entirely agree with you young man. I have met many people in my long life and it has been a long life. A life longer than you can possibly imagine. I have met many who talk of spirituality but who are the furthest from it. My mother used to say there are devils in disguise out there, best bit of advice she ever gave me."

"It is not wise to be cynical."

"It is not being cynical young man, it is the truth."

"My guru tells me that he is connected to me wherever I am and he is guiding me, I am love, everything I do is good."

"What good things have you done?"

"Things like this. I am teaching you my wisdom, making you aware. I am on a mission to save the planet to make people aware of the destruction we are doing."

The old woman laughs. "Let me give you some elderly advice young man. If you want to save the planet I would suggest you focus on changing yourself. If human beings pay attention to who they are and work at understanding themselves then the planet will be saved, that's all it will take. Just let the planet be, leave it alone, it can take care of itself very well." She pauses. "Can I ask you a question?" The young man's eyes fill with fear, his smile full of bravado. "What is love?"

The young man laughs. "Being nice, being kind."

"I'm not feeling the love, love has feeling and I'm not feeling it from you." He laughs. "Explain it to me."

"It's… being nice." He struggles to find his words. "And kind and helping people." There is a level of detachment in his words that cannot be disguised.

"My advice to you dear is when you understand love you can teach your wisdom. I suggest you continue your journey and search for the love, the love that is life. The only love, the pure unconditional type of love, when you can tell me what that kind of love feels like then you will be ready to truly help people."

He places his hand on her head. "Guru, please help this woman to understand, she is consumed by the dark side."

"Young man. Wisdom comes from losing things, from pain comes contentment, from that level of contentment comes spirituality, from spirituality comes unconditional love."

The young man smiles as he touches the old woman's forehead.

"I wish for this woman that one day she sees the world with new eyes."

The old woman smiles.

"If you weren't such a good looking young man I would give you a good telling off."

He removes his hand and continues at his snail like pace to the bathroom.

# CHAPTER 12

# Change begins

"Would you like some coffee?" Molly is lost in her dreamlike state. "Coffee?" Jake questions.

"No, I'm fine thanks."

"What are you doing?"

"I'm thinking."

"You never think."

She turns back as the clouds change to a hazy grey. "I know."

Jake unclasps his seatbelt, nature is calling him and he has no choice but to go.

"Can you get me a glass of water please?" Molly asks.

"Where am I supposed to get water from?"

"Ask Scarlet."

"You mean the stewardess."

"Yes Scarlet."

"Ok."

He turns to exit at the same time as a rather portly gentleman is exiting from the opposite side of the aisle. He is trying to squeeze past the young fifteen year old boy who has been scribbling away in his notepad for the entire journey.

"Can I get past?" The portly man is unable to move backwards or forwards as the Middle Eastern gentleman rests to the left of him, his eyes closed. "I need to get out," he states with a hint of aggression towards the young boy.

The young boy looks up awkwardly trying to move his legs.

"For God's sake just get up boy."

"I can't."

"I swear if you don't move out of that seat I will move you myself."

An older man stands in the aisle behind. He is tall. He looks down on the guy in front of him.

"Please don't speak to my son like that."

The portly man who is now a little red in the face presses the intercom and stands in silence waiting for the stewardess to assist. Scarlet approaches carrying a tray of water.

"He won't move out of his seat."

"If you would like to sit back down sir I will organize it for you."

"Sit back down, why would I want to sit back down?"

"I need to assist the young boy in getting out of his seat."

"I'll assist him."

"My son is disabled, if you could give us five minutes we will get him out of the seat."

Jake is standing watching the drama unfold as Molly taps him. She points to the water on Scarlet's tray. Jake ignores her, not quite knowing what to do he turns sitting back down. He is deep in thought.

Scarlet lifts the young boy with the assistance of his father.

"Anyone would think you were disabled and being a pain," the young boy laughs at Scarlet's statement. She chuckles as she places him down in the seat behind Jake.

The portly man is out of the row and walking up the aisle. He doesn't look back.

Scarlet gives the young boy a glass of water.

"I'm sorry about that sir," Scarlet apologises.

The young boy smiles as he speaks, "It's ok, he doesn't understand."

Jake stands, he cannot wait any longer. He cannot stand anymore thinking. He glances to Molly who is staring out of the window. She is different to how he has seen her before. There is a detachment about her, it's as if she has withdrawn from him into another world.

He unbuckles his seatbelt and stands. A walk is the only thing on his mind right now. A walk away from his head and his situation.

He steps into the aisle. Scarlet notices him coming towards her, she moves forwards giving him one of her smiles. His thoughts have changed from work, to himself, to his past, to his life now. It's as if everything that had ever taken place before was revealing itself for the first time. Bombarded by a million different situations, relationships, meetings and break ups, business successes and failures. As if it was all being revealed to him in this moment. Like watching a movie of his life, where he is the main character and he is seeing who he is for the first time. This character needs to be in control, this person needs to be in control of everything.

I am tired of this journey and I'm tired of life. His thoughts surprise him; one thought is followed by another. Why am I tired of life? He looks to the other passengers as he passes. A mixture of people from all ages and all walks of life, all nationalities and all religions.

His eyes meet the eyes of the middle-aged portly man who is pacing up and down in the back galley area. There is an urgency and anger in every movement.

For a moment he thinks upon middle age. What is middle age? A state of shock consumes him. Oh god! I'm having a mid-life crisis! His thoughts move forwards. What is a mid-life crisis? He is surprised by the speed in which his mind responds to him in the way in which it is revealed to him. As his thoughts begin and never end, providing him with an influx of information.

When we have a mid-life crisis, it is that moment when we have worked for a number of years to survive and there comes a point where the body becomes tired. The mind becomes tired, the emotions have experienced many things and the struggle sets in. The extreme things people do when they reach this age are because they want to feel life, they want to feel passion, they want to feel love, they want to see their dreams in front of them with a world awaiting to receive them. But they are at a point where their dreams have been tossed by the wayside so that they can maintain the life that they have been conditioned to live. The life of a home, a family. For some this is all they can maintain due to money, but others who have money, who have material things, they still have their dream buried somewhere deep in their soul, the ones who live in the convenience of luxury, of easiness, in a world where reality doesn't exist, for without the struggle there is no reality.

They look for new things, new people to invigorate them, to make them feel life again, instinctively on the deepest level they know that time is running out, death is closer than ever before and the will to feel life on every level consumes them; they begin to realize what is real and what isn't. As real is what we desire on the deepest level.

How do I find real? Inside of you, that is the only place you will find it. It is to be found nowhere else. Connect with your source, connect with your power and the journey you will find yourself on in the later part of your life, will be a life fulfilling your dreams. There isn't so far to run, take the energy of the first half of your life, all the experiences, all the love, all the passion, all the joy and all the pain.

All serve a purpose; use those experiences to transcend to a higher state of consciousness.

Your mind is willing you, it is revealing it to you on every level, showing you that there is more, that is why you feel the desire, to live, to create. It knows that you have not reached your destiny.

Find out who you are because if you don't, you will never know. What a waste that would be to spend an entire lifetime searching externally, getting to know the world around you and everyone else, but never ever knowing who you really are.

What a waste.

# CHAPTER 13

# Your work is your creation

Jake reaches the bathroom but another hurdle awaits him, a queue of people. He decides to stick it out and wait in the hope that no one speaks to him. He turns his back to the queue facing towards the front of the aircraft, glancing at his watch.

An elderly gentleman joins the queue.

"I had a watch like that. It cost me four dollars in Hong Kong. I was in the navy."

Jake glances at his expensive watch.

"Do you mind if I lean against the wall there young man?"

Jake obliges willingly at the suggestion that he is a young man and lets the old man take his place.

"It's not great getting old you know."

Jake smiles.

"What do you do?"

"Films. I make films," Jake states with an air of tediousness.

"Interesting! I used to be a school caretaker. I loved my job, you know it's so important to love your job."

Jake nods for a moment wishing he was a school caretaker.

"I couldn't wait to get up in the mornings. 4 a.m. every morning, I woke before the alarm clock rose, that's how much I loved it – I miss it you know, you miss work when it's gone."

The look on Jake's face tells he is not convinced.

"My partner loved Christmas, since they always gave me a hamper. Fortnum and Masons. It had everything in it, didn't cost us a lot at Christmas because of that hamper, we were lucky."

Jake looks to the queue; there is a look of frustration at the speed it is going, as always much slower than it needed to be.

"It's our last trip you know. Our last trip together."

Jake doesn't respond he just gives back his half interested smile. The old man isn't in the conversation he is looking out of the window lost in his thoughts.

"My partner, she's dying."

"I'm sorry!"

"It's ok we are both old. I'm eighty-seven and she's eighty-five. We've had a great life; we loved each other you know. We never married. No need to when you love each other. They only marry now for money. You know the only way to know if you love someone, to really know, is losing them, you have to lose people to know. I lost her for ten years and then she came back to me. I waited, and she waited, but we didn't know each other was waiting. Life's funny really, we never say what we feel until it's too late, or we make assumptions when someone disappears and most of the time those assumptions are wrong. Never make assumptions!"

"At least you got there in the end," Jake surprises himself at his engagement in the conversation.

The queue has moved and the old man is next.

"Go on son, it's your turn you were before me." He gestures for Jake to go first.

"No, it's ok, I can wait."

"You go, I'd like to stand here for a little while."

Jake nods and makes his way to the toilet as the portly man approaches from the back of the aircraft, he makes his way back down the aisle bumping the shoulder of the old man.

"Excuse me is the word!" the old man shouts behind him. The portly man continues without reaction.

The old woman makes her way through the cabin. She is holding onto every chair back along the way, she makes it half way down the aisle and waves her hand in the air trying to gain attention. "Woo hoo!" she shouts to the old man.

He turns looking down the aisle, his face beams affectionately at the madness in her movement.

"You ok?"

He laughs. "Yes, I'm ok. Just having a think dear."

She nods turning as she pootles back to her seat.

Jake exits, holding the door open for the old man.

"You just missed my love. She was here, she came looking for me. Do you have a lady?"

Jake nods.

"What's her name?"

"Molly."

"That's a nice name."

Jake smiles and moves slightly to make way for the old man to continue on his journey.

"Never sacrifice the one you love, no matter what it takes. Wait, make sure you are with the one you love; you know if you love her, you know in here. There are different kinds of love, you can love many but only one in that way, some people never have it in a lifetime. If you get it never let it go because it is meant for you in this lifetime, maybe those others are some unfinished business from another life, that you mistake for love, make sure it's right."

He punches Jake's stomach as if he had been given a new lease of life and was warming up in preparation for his big fight. "Nice meeting you." Before he finishes his sentence he is in the toilet, closing the door.

Jake is a little dazed as he walks back down the aisle, the cabin is silent. Some people are writing, some are staring into space thinking. Jake thinks about his encounter with the old man, he thinks how happy he was, how he loved his job. Jake has money, a successful career, and respect from his peers but why doesn't he feel the happiness that the old man feels?

As he makes his way back through the cabin, he catches a family laughing, for a moment he appreciates the beauty in their conversation, they are talking, something he realizes he hasn't seen for a long time – a conversation.

He looks up realizing he has walked past his seat. He can see the top of Molly's head as he approaches, see she is looking down, writing.

"How's it going?" Molly doesn't flinch. "You become a writer now?"

"Sorry! I have so many thoughts in my head, things I didn't know were there, it's amazing."

"I know, I live with them everyday." She carries on oblivious to Jake's comment. "Do you think I'm controlling?"

Molly doesn't look up, her head is consuming her, a queue of thoughts are waiting impatiently to be translated onto the page. To reveal the answers to the questions that are popping up by the minute, questions about her life.

"Do you think I'm controlling?" Jake urges.

Molly glances to him, her mind still on the book; her pen poised in position waiting for that moment when she is brave enough to reveal the things her mind is desperate to tell her.

"What?"

"Do you think I'm controlling?" Jake asks with a hint of reservation.

"Yes!" Molly states matter of factly.

"What do you mean?"

"Yes, you are controlling."

"I don't think I am."

"You are. You have to control everything."

"I'm not controlling." He sits back staring at the seat back in front of him. "I don't think I feel things."

He reaches out touching Molly's arm. She doesn't look up. He takes his arm away as those words, which seemed so daunting, are replaced by more fearsome words for these words are nothing but the truth.

"I do not feel."

Molly turns to Jake who is staring at the back of the seat in front of him.

"I'm going to be a writer." Jake doesn't respond, he is transfixed in a nonchalant manner to the seat that is his entertainment. "I'm going to be a writer! I was born to write. I love it!"

Jake doesn't take his gaze from the back of the seat.

"We discussed this ages go, we can't afford for you to do that."

"I don't care."

He sits up looking at Molly.

"The most interesting journey of our life is understanding who we are, how we function, how our emotions work and the complexities of our own minds, once we know this everything else falls into place. It begins with living your dream. I don't care. I am going to be a writer, I am going to live my dream, no one has to read it, if I am writing, I am a writer."

"What about the shop, your clients?"

"I will make it work. I waste so much time on doing things that are nothing in those moments, all that time socializing on the computer, looking at everybody else's life. I will write and I will work in the shop in the day. I will live my dream, so the movie of my life has a fantastic ending."

"What are you going to write?"

"I don't know, whatever comes through me."

"Writers know what they're going to write. They are trained properly in the process."

"I will learn as I go along,"

"What if you can't do it?"

"I can. I know I can. If you want something and you apply your willpower nothing is impossible."

"I'm serious. You are getting carried away with all of this. It's not reality."

Molly laughs.

"You don't understand, this is reality. This is what my heart and mind are telling me. I know I have been living a lie. I have been pretending, I didn't understand. We have been living in a prison cell."

Jake looks confused.

"This is freedom, doing what you love is freedom. Acknowledging it and making it happen is all under your own control, you have the power in you, we all do. I can see how simple it is now. I want to understand how my emotions work so I can use them to enhance my life rather than deplete me."

"Look when we get home you will see all of this differently. Whenever you go on holiday you get all these big ideas and then you go home and normal life resumes and you forget all about them."

"No this is different. I'm doing it, we've been asleep all of our life – do you know that we have been asleep, but no more!"

# CHAPTER 14

# Creation completed

Scarlet makes her way through the cabin collecting the glasses spotted throughout the cabin. The old couple sit holding hands gazing out of the window.

"How are you doing?"

"It was a good final flight." The old woman responds with an air of contentment.

"I know it's time."

"It's time for a new adventure."

Scarlet smiles.

"I will miss you."

"You still have Albert, he's got a long while left yet, look after him for me won't you dear."

Scarlet smiles. "I promise." Scarlet hugs her holding her tightly. The old woman pulls back.

"There is something you can do for me, that good looking chap over there." She points to the man she encountered earlier. "He needs some lessons in life otherwise he is going to hurt a lot of people."

Scarlet studies him as the attendant's buzzer interrupts her thoughts. She smiles, nodding as she makes her way to the passenger demanding her attention. She reaches the young disabled boy.

"What can I do for you young sir?"

The young boy laughs.

"You can wait on me like you are supposed to."

Scarlet laughs differently, it's a laugh of familiarity.

"Anyone would think you were disabled."

He laughs even louder.

"I have finished," the young boy hands her his writings, his pad is full.

"Who's been a busy boy?"

"A lot has happened in the past month. I have been working really hard and things are changing. I have more strength and greater mental focus."

Scarlet smiles.

"Keep up the good work. No slacking!"

"Joe's beating me, he understands better than I do."

"Everyone has their own personal journey. The journey is yours and yours alone to walk at the pace you need. Gaining the understanding when the time is right, there is no knowing it better or not knowing it better, it is what it is right now for you."

"He's still beating me."

Scarlet smiles endearingly at his youthful nature.

"Thanks!" The young boy smiles.

"No. Thank you! The most entertaining thing on this flight today was the look on the guy's face when he realized you couldn't walk."

The young boy laughs as Scarlet rubs his hair as a mother does to her child. She walks away.

"Joe, how are you doing?"

The dark-haired Cary Grant look-alike has his head down, writing. Scarlet waits as he scribbles furiously. He pauses for a moment then continues, finally putting the full stop in place.

"I'm done. The tools are really helping me. I have done it everyday."

"It's great for stepping outside of yourself as you see it from a third party perspective. When you detach from the emotions, you see everything clearly. Rather than being in the movie you are watching the movie, you see everything about the character that you are and you will understand differently.

"Writing is the key to understanding your situation, your emotions enabling you to create the change. When you put your thoughts onto paper they are no longer thoughts going around in your head, they have been put out into the world, externalized, they can no longer hurt you."

The man listens intensely.

"It's true, I have seen so many things lately and it's all making sense to me. The mind, the emotions. I understand how I function, and the detachment. It enables me to trust my instincts more. I'm not blinded by other people's thoughts and feelings.

"I'm trusting my own judgment and I know what I want and I know I can do it.

"I have no doubt, not in an arrogant way but in a way

that I am empowered by knowing myself. I see now how lost I was. When you focus on everyone else you become everyone else's and you lose yourself."

Scarlet smiles.

"That's so great. Well done! You deserve it for all the work you have put in. Patience and endurance."

"I hate patience and endurance."

Scarlet giggles.

"It's the answer to it all. Things will only come when the time is right. Master patience and endurance and life is simple, things will only come to you when you are ready, when you are connected to your mind and your emotions are calm you will hear the call. Put in the work today, stay focused on your objective and tomorrow will bring itself."

The man's face shows he has heard these words a thousand times and yet he would prefer anything than having to hear them again. "When someone you believe in believes in you anything is possible. Believe there is no way you can fall and you will not fall."

Scarlet smiles.

"I believe in you."

# CHAPTER 15

# Life is simple

" Life has new meaning – you wake up and suddenly you understand unconditional love. You know the importance of loving you. Only when you can love unconditionally can you truly love another with balance, giving them the best of you and the beauty of you.

"Can't you see the beauty in it. The beauty in life, we haven't lived, we haven't loved we haven't understood anything. We are living in a dream world, a dream that we believe is reality, but it is in fact unreality.

"Reality is in understanding you, understanding your behaviour, your nature, we are the same as nature, nature understands. Simplicity that's what they mean. Keep it simple, don't complicate it.

"We complicate things, as human beings we don't trust in any of it. We have to control it and it's in the controlling that we lose control. I get it. Do you get it?"

Molly pauses for a second but not long enough for Jake to respond.

"Do you know your nature?" He says nothing. "Do you know your nature?"

"Of course I do – I'm a control freak." He laughs at his own joke.

"OK what does that mean to you and others around you?"

"I was joking!"

"Why?"

"I was joking!"

"No that was real. Why?" Molly probes.

"I don't know. I don't think about it."

She stares at him.

"I feel." He pauses for a moment. "I don't know what, I just need to know what's going on."

"But why?"

"I don't know." There is a level of detachment in his words.

"No, 'I don't know', isn't good enough. You owe it to yourself and those around you to know who you are. I get it, when we know who we are we can turn the negatives into positives and everything in our world becomes better. You don't have the turmoil of you, you only have to deal with the turmoil of life and that is the beautiful turmoil, it is what makes us grow as human beings.

"Do you know we are so lucky, we have the gift of life and we are beginning to understand. For the first time I understand, the key to it all is understanding."

"Why would I ever want to delve there?" Jake responds his enthusiasm fading.

"That is where the answers lay, no one can give it to you, no shrink, no parent, no friend, only you. You have all of the answers inside of you. You are the power, you just need to go there and question, and you will understand, it is so simple."

"You are sounding like one of those guru types who doesn't really live in reality." Jake laughs at his own joke.

"No, don't do that, don't brush it off as if it's nothing. How can you say that when you haven't tried it? When you have experienced it and it doesn't work then you can say that. What are you so afraid of?"

"I'm not afraid."

"Then why don't you do this? Why don't you breathe and go into your mind. Clear the clutter, write and understand. What else have you had to do up here? Do you not want to live life to the full, without restriction?"

"It's not possible, everyone's messed up that's the way life is." Jake picks up his notepad.

"How do you know when you haven't even tried? How do you know it can't be the other way and everyone can resolve his or her issues? That's the easy way out saying everyone's messed up, that's weakness. No one is messed up, they just don't understand their nature or their emotions and how they work, because we are never taught it. No one is born messed up. That is wrong. They know what we are told, love should be in its external form. I'm talking about love of you. That's it! It's love of the self, until you have that how can you ever truly love anyone else, they will only ever have a part of you instead of all of you. When they know love none of the turmoil will exist."

"None of it works, if it did everyone would be doing it." He takes his attention to his notepad as he flicks through the empty pages.

"As humans we are lazy, we want the quick fix but there is no quick fix it doesn't exist. It takes constant effort, it takes hard work, it takes determination and it takes the will and want to change, I get it and I want it."

She pauses.

"It's understand yourself or die."

"Oh God! Why do you have to be so dramatic?"

Molly's enthused voice begins to spill out over the heads of the other passengers, drawing attention.

"I'm not being dramatic. If you understand yourself you live, if you don't you will never truly live the life you are destined for – it's logic. Look at how many people have depression; they are depressed because they don't understand it. We are never taught how to deal with it, we are just pumped with pills, when depression is the most natural thing in the world.

"We are taught a million different things but where is the lesson in school giving us the tools to understand ourselves, when we live with ourselves everyday. That is the biggest problem for most people, dealing with themselves. It's life or death."

Jake sits thinking.

"Do you want to live the rest of your life with frustration and the pain of the past?"

He doesn't answer.

"Well I don't. I want to understand, I want to live life to the full. I want the here and the now, the present. I want to give the best of me to others, not burden them with my restrictions and I can only do that when I know me. I feel like I have woken up and suddenly I understand unconditional love. You know the importance of loving you, for only when you can love you can you truly love another with balance, giving them the best of you, the beauty in you. I felt it in that moment when we closed our eyes. I felt love like I have never felt love before."

"You sound to me like you are losing your mind, like you are about to have some sort of breakdown."

"No I'm having a breakthrough, I feel like I'm bursting out of one world into another."

Just think of all the ills in the world. They all begin with a depression on some level and that comes from our emotions. When we understand the fear goes away. Understand your own emotions, you won't become fearful, you won't get depressed and you won't be sad or sick and if you drop dead then that's destiny. Come on you are a logical person. It's logic."

"Stop trying to change me, I'm ok." He closes his notepad.

Scarlet pauses collecting the food tray from Jake. 'How did you enjoy your food sir?"

"It was very good. Thank you!"

She looks to Molly. "Madam how was your food?"

"It was amazing," Molly smiles.

"What did you like best?" She looks to Jake.

"The Empower and Elevate water." Scarlet smiles

"Yes that's a good one. We change them on every flight."

"Why would you change it, it's good," Jake states with an air of agitation.

"Everything changes, change is the only thing that is constant. Are you the same person that you were yesterday, or the same person as you were before you got on this flight?"

Jake pauses for moment thinking.

"Yes and no. I'm me, but my experiences have been different so I see some things differently."

"If your experiences are different then you change, you cannot not change, it's a process of evolution. These are external changes that's why you remain the same inside and the experiences change you but you hold on to parts of what went before."

Jake stares at Scarlet.

"Change is the only constant, embrace it and life will be easier."

Molly looks to Scarlet in recognition as she looks down to her notepad playing the words over in her head.

"Change is the only constant, embrace it and life becomes simple."

# CHAPTER 16

# The Future

Molly rests her head against the window, each cloud a mixture of darkness and grey. The clouds weep as the rain lashes against the window, each droplet lit by the calm light from the moon reflecting the many different journeys that have been taken.

She takes her thoughts to the passengers, the passengers that she has spent the past eleven hours observing. The passengers that have become her companions for they have been on the same journey, they have an understanding of the process, they have experienced the wonder of no choice, one of the greatest things one can experience.

She thinks for a moment 'no choice', do we only change when we have no choice, as human beings? If we had the choice would we make the effort to change? She thinks about Jake and how he hangs on to what he knows, how this experience has changed him but not in the dramatic way that it has changed her.

Her mind wanders to the why? Why has she embraced

it and he hasn't? Maybe she is at a different place to him, maybe she is ready, or maybe he's afraid of what lays beneath the surface deep on the ocean floor.

Maybe the darkness of the deep scares him or maybe he just believes that he knows it, that there is nothing more than what is presented before him, in front of him at this time.

She takes her attention to the family at the beginning, the family that reminded her of her own family.

The brother and sister relationship, the competitiveness and the comfortableness. The young boy assists his sister, his plane safely tucked under his arm as he holds the paper steady for her as she scribbles in the only way a four-year-old can: without thought, without restriction, with freedom of failure, failure doesn't exist in the eyes of a child.

She thinks about the environment they are in and how much depends on our environment.

She takes her pen and writes in her notepad. 'If your environment doesn't make you flourish, change it.'

Her attention is taken by the young disabled boy, he struck her from that very first moment. His humour, his affliction. How can he be so upbeat when he has so much to contend with? She watches as he sits calm and content. His writing flowing since the moment he boarded the plane. It's as if he had a world inside him, which was just waiting to come to life.

She thinks about how a physical restriction channels the energy differently. If focused on how it can deplete a person. She thinks about being in his situation, how she would deal with it, would she be focused and external or would she delve into the depths of despair and depression, seeing no way out.

Her initial thought was 'I would want to kill myself,' and within a second it changed to 'No, I would want to connect to my mind. I would want to understand the power I had within me to create the change, to channel my energy differently to create in a different way.'

The moment is interrupted by the night sky. A clap of thunder announces the emergence of hail as the rain transforms into thousands of tiny diamonds. Molly gazes into the darkness as she thinks about how much energy she has wasted in her life on things that didn't really matter.

A fit of giggles runs throughout the aircraft. As she turns behind her she sees the two teenagers laughing hysterically. They are writing on a notepad, one writes then they laugh, and then the next writes, laughing even more.

She taps Jake on the shoulder as he stirs. He moves his legs to the side to let her pass, she pulls the covers up to his shoulders and for a moment she realizes how much she loves him. How he drives her insane but how childlike he is, how afraid he is, she places a gentle kiss on his forehead as she makes her way out into the aisle.

There is a quiet energy running throughout the cabin, it is silent, there is a gentle humming of voices like a bee buzzing around a beautiful flower on a summer's day, there is a contentment; there is a calmness.

She makes her way to the toilet as she glances at the people she has met along the way. The young man who walks at the pace of a snail, who is chatting to people giving them his life wisdom, continues to do so. The middle-aged woman who has endured hours without a drink sits writing, whilst her husband – his head still heavy at the thought – has found his escape with his blanket and pillow. The old couple who have sat talking non-stop for the entire journey and who are still talking non-stop. The portly obnoxious man sits staring out of the window, there is a resignation in his eyes, a look that says I have been defeated and I am resigned to surrendering to the moment. His notepad sits in the seat pocket in front of him the pen still sealed in its wrapping.

Molly feels an urgent need to tell him what he is missing, how quickly his life would be realized if he took pen to paper, how none of it really matters now, it is the past but she also realizes that she cannot do this, she has no right to do this, it is his journey and his alone. She cannot control another person's destiny no matter how much she wants to tell him that he has the answers to it all, he can lose the anger as quickly as it manifested, a trigger maybe somewhere way back in his childhood, a careless moment where a parent doesn't think and dismisses something important to him. A moment where he had put all of his energy and love into something and it was destroyed in an instance, shattering his belief in the world but even more tragically in himself.

She wanted to tell him that he can use this emotion for the positive, he can flip it as easily as flipping a coin.

How does she know this?

She knows this because her emotions feel calm and her head feels strong, she feels a sense of love for the people around her, how can that be wrong?

The intercom clicks.

"Ladies and gentlemen can you please return to your seats as we will be experiencing some heavy turbulence."

Molly continues as she thinks back to every person that has ever crossed her path, to how they played a part in her growth, how they helped her to evolve. For some unknown reason she feels thankful for all of them, for the ones that were like flowing rivers, where she felt she had been swept away with nothing to hold onto, where she had no choice but to go with the flow.

Her mind flips to the others, the ones who reassured her, who comforted her through her pain and the others who inflicted more pain than she ever imagined possible.

Maybe that is why relationships are misunderstood. Maybe some serve as a completion only to a chapter, maybe others serve as a beginning.

She looks to the light as the red engaged signal lights up on the toilet door. She stands gazing out of the tiny window into the night sky, into the darkness that resides at 35,000 ft. The darkness with its tiny shimmering lights each one holding a huge possibility for any second it can explode into a million different stars, a million different energies, all with the same potential. To be magnificent.

As the door opens she is stopped in her tracks. A Middle Eastern man exits the bathroom. He nods a slow nod as he holds the door open for her. She smiles as she takes it from him, her hand gently brushing against his. Touch she thinks for a moment the power of touch, to touch another human being, the powerful touch of healing.

"The heart." His words are deep and delivered as if in slow motion enabling the viewer to enjoy every second of this beautiful moment. "The heart is the first thing to form when we are born and the last thing to stop when we die."

Molly is transfixed.

"You understand your heart and you understand your mind, when both are in balance you understand love."

He takes his hand and places it on her forehead, her body slips into a trancelike state as he removes his hand and walks away.

She closes the door behind her as she sits on the toilet. There are no thoughts in her head only feelings, her mind is still and her heart is listening.

A loud knock on the door interrupts the moment.

"Madam, could you please return to your seat we will be experiencing some heavy turbulence very shortly."

Molly stands and washes her hands, she looks down as she examines them, seeing within them the passing of time like reading tree rings revealing the true age of the tree. There is but one thought in her head. Time escapes no one.

She unlocks the door to be greeted by the dark-haired man she met at the beginning of the journey.

"Hello again!" he states with a new found enthusiasm.

"Hi."

"Did you beat the challenge?" he asks

"Sorry?"

"The challenge at the beginning. Don't die before you have lived, don't live before you have died," he states with an air of satisfaction.

She thinks for a moment. "Yes! I get it."

He smiles.

"I have to live!" She looks to the young man and grabs his arms with an uncontrollable excitement. "I have to live the life I was born to live. I want everyone to feel this."

He laughs.

The intercom clicks as Scarlet interrupts the moment.

"Ladies and gentlemen, please return to your seats and fasten your seatbelts. We will be experiencing some heavy turbulence so please remain seated and ensure that your seatbelts are securely fastened."

Molly glances to the young man as she makes her way back through the cabin, following the floor lights that lead the way.

The aircraft shudders, a wobble, a shake and a dip. She grabs onto the seat back of the young couple, a shudder, a wobble, a shake, a turn. The aircraft banks to the left, she holds on unable to move, her eyes glance at the young couples' notepad as she takes her attention to the words as a means to steady her in the midst of all this chaos.

'Things I love about you.

The way you look like a little bunny rabbit when you get angry – Jessica

The way you don't like sharing your chips with anyone – Andy

The way you laugh at things that aren't funny – Jessica

The way you hug your cup when you are drinking your hot chocolate – Andy

The way you burp and then pretend it's me – Jessica

The way you don't take a breath when you are drinking a drink – Andy'

Molly feels the emotion inside of her building, the tears for the innocence, the beauty in expressing your feelings. A hand touches her shoulder as Scarlet urges her to go back to her seat, supporting her final steps back to Jake.

Scarlet glances to the young girl, who has her eyes closed and is breathing, the young girl who was consumed by fear at the start of this journey. Scarlet reaches out touching her forehead, the young girl opens her eyes and smiles.

"Are you ok?"

She looks to Scarlet nodding.

"I never asked you your name, what is your name?"

The young girl is calm as she speaks. "Charlotte. My name is Charlotte."

"It was a pleasure to meet you Charlotte."

Scarlet turns to walk away.

"I wrote…" Scarlet turns back to Charlotte. Charlotte hesitates before speaking. "I wrote him a letter, a handwritten letter of how I feel so he understands."

"I understand."

# CHAPTER 17

# New Life

The plane shudders as a flash of white light streaks through the aircraft, a bubble of air bursts tossing it from left to right like a waltzer at a fun fair. One minute you are certain it is going one way then suddenly a jerk, a tug, a shudder and you are catapulted in another direction.

The intercom clicks and Scarlet's voice echoes. "Ladies and gentlemen, I apologise for the turbulent conditions we are currently passing through a thunderstorm and we will endeavour to take you out of this situation as quickly as possible."

Scarlet glances to the woman seated in front of her, giving her permission to begin.

The woman with the purple dress and the radiant smile, the woman who has the aura of an angel sent from heaven above. Her strong American accent echoes through the aircraft, the type of voice that if you listen to for a while your ears become accustomed to. You find a comfort in it, a sort of background noise that is like music to the ears, a soothing, sensual sound; sound that is spoken with such honesty, such beauty and such truth, as her voice is projected over the loudspeaker.

"My husband is incredible, I have two girls. My husband and I met at a work conference. We had spoken on the phone a couple of times about a project we were working on, me in Denmark and him in New York and we finally got the chance to meet up. We had our meeting and chatted like we were old friends. I remember him commenting on how perfect I looked in purple. Purple is my favourite colour.

"Well, we left the conference and didn't see each other for two years, that was that. At the time I was a single parent with one daughter. A beautiful daughter, full of life, too much life to be honest. But her energy and enthusiasm for life was exhilarating. You wanted to listen to her all the time, she could hold anyone's attention, she knew all the tricks.

"I always wondered if she learnt them from me, or whether they were just instinct. I always wondered, do you have your own instincts at the age of five, but in her case I think she was always one step ahead of me."

Scarlet smiles, encouraging her to continue.

"Well my daughter died, she was five. It was the day of her funeral, everyone had left the house and I was sitting on the sofa, life was dead. I never thought I would ever get off my sofa again when the doorbell rang. I ignored it and it rang again, I ignored it again, the dog began to bark, it rang again and again, the dog went crazy I resisted and it stopped."

"I continued to gaze out of the window at the back of my house. Her bike sat on the patio where she had left it three days ago. The day I told her to come in and wash her hands after she had dug up a few worms in the garden. I could see her sitting there grinning at me, rubbing the mud between her palms.

"A hand appears on the glass of the window, cupping around a face, two eyes peer in at me. It's the postman. My first thought was what is he doing in my garden? He taps on the window. I cannot stay on my sofa I have to get up and go to the door, he can see me, I have no escape; I cannot ignore him, how rude would that be. I get up from the chair move, grab the dog and open the door. 'Miss Malony?'

"Yes, that's me, always has been, always will be. He picks up the bouquet of flowers that lay on the floor next to him.

"More flowers, I told everyone no flowers, they are beautiful, mauves all mauve flowers every single one of them was mauve. It almost seemed like every flower you could ever purchase in mauve was in that bouquet, these are from someone who knows me, they should have listened to what I said to make a donation to the children's charity. Flowers are of no use. I take the flowers, I am angry but I cannot resist smelling them, they are beautiful, the smell touches me, I mean touches me in a way I hadn't been touched before, they were stronger, they were powerful, they were vibrant and they were alive. I gazed at the flowers, the postman stood staring holding out his pen and paper.

"I tucked the bouquet under my arm trying to clench the paper, scribbling an unreadable signature on the paper. I looked at my signature. Who was this person? Who was I now? I have no one, I was alone, that person on that piece of paper was alone in the world, twenty four hours ago she was a mum, a carer, a playmate, a friend, a teacher, a disciplinarian. I was a mum and I am no longer a mum, you have no idea how that felt looking at my name. Who was this person now? I have no idea.

"I grabbed the flowers, thanked the postman and closed the door. I turned the key and leant against the door looking at the room, the empty silent room.

"The dog looked up at me waiting, waiting for something to happen, waiting for her tail to be tugged, to be ridden like a horse, to be chased around the house, to be hugged like she had never been hugged before, a child's hug is so much more real to an animal than an adult hug because they have no boundaries. They see the animal in its purity as a living thing not as a dog that is smelly and naughty and destructive, they see all the good that exists.

"I tap the dog on the head, she looks disappointed slumping onto my white rug on the floor, 'Get off!' I stop. Why am I telling the dog to get off the rug? In my moment of complete and utter loss, I am still telling the dog to get off the rug something I have done every day for the past four years.

"I tap the rug for the dog to get back onto it, she doesn't. I tug at her collar to pull her on. I shouldn't have shouted at the dog all the time, she feels uncomfortable, she won't budge, I shout at her to get onto the rug! She runs out of the room. I am losing my mind."

The woman turns to Scarlet. "Am I boring everyone?"

"I feel blessed that you are sharing this with us. I want to hear the story." Scarlet smiles a comforting smile.

"I know it can be boring hearing people's sob stories but this isn't I can assure you." She smiles again a warmth resonates through her words.

"Nobody's story is a sob story, they are just stories, our story is all we leave behind. It's life in its purest form, it's real and it exists and our lives need to be shared."

Scarlet reaches out touching the woman's hand, the softness of her touch reflects in the woman's eyes. There is a distance in her eyes, as if she has travelled far away.

"I glance at the flowers, they are beautiful. I like them. I like the fact that I have flowers really. I open the card and begin to read the note which is written in mauve pen… 'Mauve is perfect, you are perfect, the day I met you was perfect, and your life will be perfect again. Perfect but with a wisdom and a knowledge that this experience is going to give you everything you need in life to understand, when you understand life becomes as close to perfect as it will ever be. I am here for you. I loved you from day one and when you are ready be it six hours, six months or six years, if you feel the same, I would love you to join me by my side to continue your journey in life with me in whatever capacity your soul needs, nothing more, nothing less. However it will work.' There was a telephone number underneath; I had no idea who it was from.

"It was the worst but also the happiest day of my life. I married him three weeks later and it's the same today as it was on day one. I thought I had found love the first time and I pretended it was right, as you do when you are unaware. This time I was more aware than I had ever been, and it was right. I knew and I couldn't ignore it. I knew at that conference, but life sort of just continued and I let it go, if you know what I mean?

"She is with me every day and I know it was the plan and that's just the way it is. All the time I speak of her with love she is alive, her life may have been short but her legacy will be magnificent."

The aircraft shudders. Scarlet clicks on the intercom.

"When we lose someone dear to us we sometimes stay in their death, we do not leave them, the pain is too much but when we celebrate who they are, what they were, what they gave us, the beautiful things that we shared they become alive. I hope you enjoyed listening to Ms Maloney's story. I heard this story when I met her on this flight a few years ago. This woman inspired me, she made me see and to believe, at the end of the day, it is all in how we choose to see it.

"A choice that lies within us all, she had found that place of peace and calm. She made the choice to embrace the beauty in the situation, feel the pain, share her story, and keep her daughter alive in the most inspiring way possible. It transformed at least one person, myself and I am sure many more of you today."

# CHAPTER 18

# Breath is life

The plane drops and a loud echo of screams resonate through the cabin. The young man grasps the side of his chair, in a slightly quicker manner than his snail like performance at the start of the journey.

The oxygen masks drop down as if from the sky above.

Babies begin to cry, hands grip the seat rests, some passengers close their eyes in the hope that all will be normal when they reawaken, this moment of uncertainty will have vanished, others are praying to whoever they look up to hoping that they can hear them, that they can guide them.

The wild winds of the storm grasp the plane pushing and pulling the aircraft like an invisible hand toying with a model plane.

"Please ensure you place the mask over any small children before placing the mask on yourself," Scarlet's voice echoes throughout the aircraft.

The young man glances to Amberley as she sits waiting

patiently as he places his mask over his head breathing exaggerated breaths. Amberley takes her mask and places it over her face, breathing gently, closing her eyes as she plays over Scarlet's words in her head. 'Close your eyes breathe and you will find the light.' She is calm, she is focused, she is hugging her fluffy plane and she is free from fear.

The plane turns hard to the left spiralling with it's nose pointed towards the vast ocean below. The young man, his breath becoming shallower by the second, reaches out grabbing the oxygen mask from Amberley's face. She remains calm as she places her hand firmly on the mouthpiece, as her strength outweighs his panic.

"I need more air."

Her father is stricken by fear, paralysed in the moment as he watches his daughter fight for her life, as the young man tugs at her mask. The tension building as he is fighting his own inner battle of flight or fight, at the last moment he stands, his duty calls, every parent has a duty of care, a duty of loyalty, a duty of responsibility of bringing a child into the world. It is for life, it is to the end, it is eternal and no one tries to take my child's life runs through his veins, as he confronts the young man.

"If you don't let go I'm going to…"

Before he can finish his sentence Amberley is reaching her arm out protecting her father from making a mistake.

The nose of the aircraft pulls up, it meets the horizon once more as he falls back down into his seat. It is climbing, it is ascending, it is giving a small moment of relief.

"Dad, I'm ok," her voice is calm and authoritative, an instruction that her father cannot ignore. She turns to the young man. "If you stay calm I will take it off and share it with you. You can take a breath and then I can take a breath, then we both live."

Amberley takes off her mask and gently places it over the young man's face.

"Now take three deep breaths and focus on here." She places her finger in the centre of his forehead. "Keep your attention focused here and think the words new life, power and strength."

He follows her instruction. The power in her breath becomes weaker, her words becoming slower.

"Now give me the mask."

She takes her hand away as he replaces it with both his hands.

"Please give me the mask," she asks panicking.

He clenches harder, his eyes fixed looking straight ahead. Her voice weakens as everything begins to fade away.

"Please give me the…"

A hand reaches out from above touching her forehead. She looks up, unable to make out the figure in front of her; the muffled sound of the cabin surrounds her, like she is in a distant world, far away from everything she has ever known.

"Amberley, take a breath."

Amberley searches for her breath.

"Good girl! Breathe."

The sounds gradually begin drifting back into reality

as she hears Scarlet's voice in the distance. Amberley breathes.

"And again, deeper, will it with all your strength, all your energy, all the passion you have inside of you."

She breathes stronger, and stronger as her eyes open.

She is met by Scarlet standing above her holding an oxygen mask over her face; her vision begins to return as she is greeted with Scarlet's comforting smile.

"Your mother called me."

Amberley smiles, she turns her head slightly looking to the young man next to her whose breathing has stabilized. A look of disappointment and disbelief swamps her face.

Scarlet interrupts the moment.

"Just focus on you, the universe will take care of itself, don't waste your energy."

Amberley turns away, taking deep breaths as the young man begins a frantic search for the last instances of air.

"My mask isn't working." He looks to Scarlet, she doesn't flinch. "Didn't you hear me – my mask, it's not working!" Scarlet pays no attention. His breathing shallows as he begins to hyperventilate.

Scarlet looks to Amberley and gestures with a subtle nod. Amberley calmly removes her mask and places it over the young man's face, as he takes a breath, his first breath of life.

Scarlet turns to the young man. "True spirituality comes from putting others first. We may think we have evolved but it is not until we are tested that we know we have evolved."

# CHAPTER 19

# Birth

Molly's only thought is death. Death is your ending and it is your beginning. Death is the curtain call. It is the final chance; it is the one that says it's now or never.

Death and fear work together, they work hand-in-hand to try to get you to understand who you are. When we do not listen to death we are taken on a journey of no return. On this life path there is no way forward, but when death speaks, we listen. He gives us our growth, our understanding, our appreciation and our love for life.

Appreciate death, understand death's purpose, it is there to show us the way. Think and question, do not disrespect death in staying with him for his purpose is to allow you to grow, to allow you to see, to allow you to understand. There is nothing to fear in death, it is our only certainty.

Death doesn't lie, he is truth, he is honesty. That is why we fear him because he doesn't pretend; we would like him to pretend. Listen to him, he is telling you I am coming, so live, make every day matter. Death is giving you life that is his purpose. If you listen to him he is giving the greatest gift, the gift of living.

Molly's train of thought is interrupted momentarily as a shard of majestic moonlight beams through the half closed window shade, which catches Molly's eyes. Jake is transfixed on Molly as her demeanour has gone from weakness to strength as she speaks. "I get it."

"Well that's the story of my life just when someone finally gets it, it's gone," Jake states.

There was little that Molly could do but surrender to the moment. She had thought about her life and where she was. How much she had learnt and what she had left to do and yet there was an understanding that she hadn't had before, an understanding of so much more of so many dimensions.

The jigsaw puzzle that she had struggled so many times with, how things appeared when she didn't want them. She did everything in her power to change them to what she wanted, from career to relationships, she realized now that if things aren't meant for you they will not stay, maybe that is what it's all about, maybe it's all planned, maybe we just have to do the work moving forward with trust.

This was a journey of reconnecting, but the reconnection felt like a rebirth. It felt like a renewal, like a caterpillar turning into a butterfly and seeing the wonder of life for the very first time.

She played over the thoughts again…

I am a believer, I know I'm a believer, but in this moment of actually feeling all of these things have I become a sceptic? Why have I become a sceptic? Because the reality of it doesn't seem believable. How could it be real? Why me? Why am I seeing these things? What is their purpose?

In that moment she found an answer.

You are being given the tools you need to continue to your destiny, they are being revealed to you because you are ready to receive and you are ready to act.

You are ready to embrace the journey. Do not be afraid there is nothing to fear, it is a guide, it is direction. It is showing you the path you need to walk for that path is for you and you alone and it is time.

Molly glances at Jake. She taps him on the shoulder.

"There is more."

He doesn't move.

"There is more, there is so much more."

His eyes remain closed.

"No more. I can't take anymore," Jake exclaims.

"I'm serious, I feel it. There are other dimensions. We are on another dimension right now. We have been transported to a deeper state of consciousness, we are being guided."

Jake looks a little spooked by the way she is behaving.

"I know this is insane, but I just know there is more."

The lights in the cabin flicker, scaring Jake into breaking the subject.

"Can't this captain fly this plane properly."

Molly takes Jake's hand. "Breathe. Use what you have learnt, it is now in the most desperate moments that you will feel its power."

Jake submits to Molly's plea and tries to breathe but all that follows is a short shallow breath.

The majority of the passengers have their eyes closed, looking up to something, their own higher power, in this moment of desperation they are looking up. Molly realizes in this moment she is looking up, she is tapping into her higher power, the higher mind.

There is no understanding in this moment, there is only trust. Every single day is unknown, every single moment is unknown, the only certainty we have in this life is death and our certainty is upon us, it is here and it is present.

The cabin is silent. There are no questions, there are no answers.

You have journeyed within your mind. You have listened to logic, you have listened to the heart. The heart is open, the mind is ready to receive, to share, to guide and to live, only with this understanding, can you truly live, can you truly love, can you truly evolve.

It is in this moment that you will understand the self. That you will realize what is real and what isn't. What love is? What life is? And how you can attain it.

It is waiting, it is ready, you are ready, you are ready to be strong to be happy with the knowledge that nothing matters, nothing really matters. Only life matters, only moments matter, only the here and now matter.

Molly has but one resounding thought in her head.

I am so grateful for this very second, just to be able to see with new eyes, to be able to understand the value of breath, to be able to walk, to hear, to love, to be given the most precious gift – the gift of life itself and what a gift it is to be aware and recognize this, not everyone is that lucky.

It is in this moment that she realizes she wants life. She wants life like she has never wanted life before.

CHAPTER 20

# Transformation

The wings flutter like a newspaper held out of a car window. A clap of thunder, an instance of lightning lights up the aircraft cabin like a thousand camera flashes as they drift into the clouds over the Hudson Bay.

The turbulent rain lashes on the window like a stream flowing across the reinforced-glass windows, turbulence treading carefully like a gentle wave, as it builds to its crescendo, the aircraft tries to power through over the crest of it. Screams echo throughout the aircraft.

The plane banks and tilts, the wing flips up and down, it's as if the plane is trying to flap its own wings. It has no choice but to be flexible. The lightning flashes as if coming from an angry disgruntled Earth, shouting its frustration, demanding to be heard as the aircraft enters the clouds.

Captain Dennis' voice echoes in the darkness…

"Good Morning! Ladies and gentlemen, may I apologize for the night sky having a tantrum tonight? She has given us a big nudge to change course so we are in the process of making the change, please hold tight and we will take you into the light as soon as possible."

A gap in the chaos lies ahead on the other side of the cloud filled sky as the aircraft is directed to this space of calm air. Darts of white light flash past the window like a thousand lightning arrows being shot all at once onto a transparent screen exploding across the window.

The aircraft becomes a lonesome creature in the midst and power of nature revealing all its beauty. As the clouds break a dazzling white tunnel begins to evolve into a tunnel in which to travel through, a tunnel to the light of lights.

As Scarlet moves throughout the cabin the windows light up as if a warning light is coming, the plane rocks as if rolling from side-to-side, people grasping their arm rests in a pathetic attempt to defy nature.

Scarlet makes her way to the front of the aircraft.

The intercom clicks.

"Ladies and gentlemen can you please remain in your seats with your seatbelts securely fastened until the seatbelt signs have been turned off."

Molly glances out of the window, in the distance an array of bluish white lights light up the midnight sky.

Jake pulls the cover over his head trying to continue with his sleep. A bolt of lightning hits the wing of the aircraft, as the plane suddenly drops in altitude, cups and plates are catapulted into the air striking the ceiling of the aircraft cabin. The cabin fills with one almighty scream as everyone hits the perfect note at the perfect time in unison as the aircraft banks to the left, turning, speeding, accelerating, faster and faster, the passengers hang onto the seat backs in front of them as they are turned onto their side.

A young child starts to cry. "I want to phone my mommy."

The lightning strikes again, the nose of the aircraft dives. The aircraft shudders from side to side suspended in mid air like a puppet on a string. Scarlet makes her way through the cabin diligently checking that all seatbelts are securely fastened.

"Good morning ladies and gentlemen," there is a long pause.

"It's evening! Can't he even get that right," Jake mutters under his breath.

Scarlet checks Jake's seatbelt as she speaks.

"It's always good morning on the Mind Flight plane because every moment is a new beginning."

Molly looks out to the wing as she sees flames blazing from the engine. It is in this moment that she knows that it's over, that it's gone, that there is no going back, her eyes are transfixed on the engine fire trying to stay alight in the midst of this storm.

Captain Dennis continues, his voice calm, slow, gentle…

"Imagine a furnace and within it is the smelting workshop of truth power and complete ability. Restoration, rebalance and with the desire to bring new life, power and total strength. And within this furnace is the place that creates, commands and forms that objective intention forged within every breath. I want you to become aware that this is the crucible that creates awareness for every part of you is comfortable. Imagine that with every in breath, breathe in to the crucible of life, a crucible kindling beginning to see a spark, the start of a small but significant fire."

Molly is listening as she watches the flames stream from the engine. All that can be heard is the sound of the engine whirring, struggling to stay alive. Some of the passengers are crying, some staring into nothingness, others holding onto each other, others are sitting silent waiting for the end, almost willing it. It is in this moment that they realize the thought of death is more painful than death itself.

The thought that in a few seconds life as you know it will be over, like a breath on a candle flame, one minute it is there the next it is gone. Extinguished, no longer alive.

Molly begins to breathe as she follows Captain Dennis' instructions, it's almost as if she has been automatically programmed to obey the instruction, she takes a deep breath as he continues.

"With every breath this fire will become more intense, with every breath. With every breath growing from a kindle, progressively this little source of light is more and more apparent, growing with every breath. Imagine that fire, that source of light. Breathe in that light, command with every breath."

Molly breathes like she has never breathed before,

whilst the majority of passengers are engulfed by fear. Molly is feeling life, life in every breath, she is feeling the power of the flame, the purity in life, the bliss of connecting to the spiritual, the awareness of life itself, the freedom.

"Breathe that air and allow it to combust into the fire of power and total strength.

"A fire of total positive strength.

"Allow this fire to light the path."

Jake sits frozen like a rabbit stuck in the headlights holding onto his seat, his hands clenched, as his fear consumes him.

"And within that stillness feel the comfortable warmth of it. Allow with every breath the strong powerful fire emit a healing sense of warm comfortableness. This is a fire of light, this is a fire of total strength and with that begin to allow strength to follow through. Allow the light of that fire emit a healing warmth. Pure and totally complete, this is the fire of warmth within every part of your mind and your body. Allow that warmth that healing energy to surround you, emanate with every breath of that healing energy."

Molly takes a deep breath as she reaches out gently touching Jake's hand, she rubs it slowly, gently as she whispers, "Breathe, just breathe with me."

Molly sees something for the first time. A vibrant white light there in front of her in the darkness of her mind. A light that radiates a peace, as she bathes in the beautiful light, there is no fear.

A voice resounds in her head as she is transported on a journey of discovery as she sees the stars, feels the water, embraces the mountains, and explores the forests. Nature is serenity and sanctity. Nature expands the mind, exhilarates the heart, softens the soul and surrounds our spirit. A mixture of every emotion that we feel. She takes us to a world of mystery, a world of wonder, a world of the unknown but where all is known. Watch nature, listen to nature, understand nature and you have the answer to life. Nature is your teacher.

She turns to Jake opening her eyes, her eyes are alive, full of radiance as she smiles serenely.

"We have been asleep all of our lives."

Jake watches as the halo of light surrounding Molly begins to fade as the flame on the engine extinguishes. Jake holds her gaze, transfixed by her beauty.

# CHAPTER 21

# Destiny

The intercom clicks, there is a long pause…

Several large flexible screens gradually un-roll from the ceiling at intervals throughout the aircraft. For a moment the passengers are brought out of their turmoil, something familiar has appeared, something from the life that they have known before. Something that reassures them, it has been thirteen hours without a television or any form of entertainment and now in this moment of desperation one appears to give them an answer. This is where they look for the answers, answers that are presented to them by the powers that be.

"Ladies and gentlemen if you could kindly pay attention to the information that will appear shortly on the screens in front of you. Focus on the horizon ahead of you, the objective and the end, remain comfortable in this uncomfortable situation. Sit back, and focus. Focus with one aim without halt to the finish line."

The cabin is filled with the most awe-inspiring music.

The screen is lit by a vibrant colourful display of dancing light.

There is something surreal and strange about this moment as the plane heads into the dancing lights. The lights that contain every essence of our life. The green of the land that nourishes us and provides us with everything we need to survive. The blue of the ocean of water, that sustains life, without it life on Earth could not exist.

Purple, the comforting colour, the higher power, the strength, the love, the spiritual. A choice of staying or returning home. It is here that you will decide what the next life will bring.

It is here that you shall find your answers. It is here that you have your choice.

The answers reveal themselves one by one across the screen…

It takes but one thing. YOU.
It all begins with that first breath.
That first breath, brings life.

When breath is mastered thinking begins.
From thinking comes learning.
From learning comes evolving.
Give yourself time.
The only place you will find your destiny is within YOU.
It is under your own control.
Your mind is the greatest power in existence.

We are all conditioned to think that we cannot be great.
But we can all be great.
Whatever comes from the depths of your mind is pure.
Save yourself precious lifetime by understanding your own mind.
Want to know more.
What have you got to lose?
Nothing.
What have you to gain?
Everything.
You have one chance.
With no re-runs.
Make the life you want.
When you take possession of your own mind.
You heal.
Everything becomes stronger.
Mentally, emotionally, physically, spiritually.
Positive instruction. Positive thought.
When you have balance of
the mind and the emotions.
You are open to the kind of love most of us very rarely experience in a life time.
Pure unconditional love.
Find the answers to the most fundamental questions of life.
Who am I? Why am I here? Where is life leading me?
How can I improve? What is my purpose?
Where do I find these answers?
Within YOU.

You will understand yourself completely enabling you to understand others, free from fear, creating a world of balance and bliss coming from truth.

You will see YOU for the first time.

Be brave. Face YOU.

Words are the window to your own personal wisdom.

Write to overcome, write to understand how you function, to understand who you are?

The words will turn your depression into divinity.

We are all beautiful human beings, it is only when we do not understand our emotions and our own minds that we lose control. See the past, as a valuable learning experience.

You are here, you are now, you are alive, where there is breath there is life, where there is life anything is possible.

You are magnificent, you are amazing, you are beautiful.

Create the change… your mind is waiting to obey your instructions.

When we understand the fear goes away.

Master the elements of patience and endurance; they are our greatest teachers.

Stay the course, no matter how much you feel like running when things get tough, this is the time to continue.

To stay, to push through, to understand for after anguish comes bliss as the higher self is revealed, nothing in your life will ever be the same again.

You see you, who you are, see what you are capable of and it will be magnificent.

It will be beyond anything you could possibly ever imagine

Are you ready to begin your journey?

# CHAPTER 22

# Transcendence

"Ladies and gentlemen," there is a warmth that comforts and a certainty that calms, there is a slowness and a depth to its projection as he speaks his first words. "I am going to guide you through what is about to take place. This is the only way, so please follow the instructions exactly as I relay them to you. Everything will be ok, when you look back on this moment you will realize nothing matters, what does it matter. I would like you to place your palms face down onto your lap."

The passengers place their palms face down.

"Close your eyes and BREATHE."

The passengers obey as the sound of a deep exhale resounds through the cabin. Each passenger's head drops as they fall into an induced sleep.

A symphony of lights, as if born from space, an operatic concert, bound towards consciousness, a reality of wonder to behold. The coloured lights, shifting, moving, like the neurons within our brains and the thoughts contained within our minds. Like ocean waves in a sea storm with the power of light, blessed with the magic of silence. Spanning many miles across the sky, this storm is a storm of silence, an impressive show beyond any other.

As the colours of the light storm, bound for the eyes of those who see it, its strident sight of colour and light directed into the mind. It brings us wonder, as grand as ocean waves, we can't keep it within our clasping hands, as a wave just turns into water as thoughts turn into feeling. As thoughts act like instances of feeling, so we see with our mind the power of thought, singularly on their own without action they are meaningless, yet that single droplet of water can bring a great wave of change, and so is the same with a thought born in the core of consciousness.

This is a window of capability, a view into the power of nature, equally paralleled by a view into the power of the mind.

The Aurora Borealis is not there for all of us to see in an instant.

The choice we make to see it is brought on by our selfless desire to seek it.

The choice lies within us, whether we choose to see it or not.

Yet the rewards await a single glimpse, if only but a second, a show of nature that can easily surpass any attempt by us to recreate it.

If the desire is present, and we choose to become

aware, we can bare witness to a power within us, a gateway to our own limitless abilities.

As powerful, as magnificent and as awe inspiring as this enigmatic dance of wave and colour we all know as the Aurora Borealis.

The passengers are gone, gone into a world deep beyond what they have always known to have existed, they are beyond all knowledge and all understanding. They are at one with the mind, with the heart, with the soul; they are one with the universe and it is in this moment that the words they thought they would want to hear only a few moments ago feel so distant from the present, for the present is purity, it is peace, it is perfection as they drift silently into bliss.

The only voice that can be heard is the voice of the captain. It is different this time, it is deeper, it is stronger, it reverberates throughout the cabin as if booming from a loudspeaker. It is slow, it is precise, it is pronouncing the words, the words that the passengers are now ready to understand…

"For most of us, death is fatal… **The ones who have been left behind.** Do not grieve, it is our time, your time will come. We are in the air, we are in your thoughts, we are in your hearts, cry the tears, release the love and channel that love into more love. Take the love that you feel for us out into the world and give it with everything you can, find the love for it is this that will heal you, it is this that will transport you, it is this that will take you on your journey of transcendence. Love until your heart breaks, for the heart with the most scars is the heart that understands the most, that can love the most.

"The answer is within you, it is your journey and yours alone – it takes

"Breathing

"Into the darkness

"Of the mind

"Where the magic of life

"Will be revealed

"A place where your emotions

"Find their balance

"The heart and mind become one

"Working in unison

"Together to create the change.

"It is only then that your destiny will be revealed to you.

"The answers are in you, for you and they are waiting to be found by you."

# Epilogue

The plane glides slowly and silently into the void, the light consumes the aircraft, a blinding light. A light that is so bright, a light that gives you no choice but to listen, a light that takes away that very moment. The light is blinding, you cannot see you can only feel. What you are feeling is peace, it is love, it is unconditional. It is the only love that we need to survive, the hardest love to find, the most impossible love to sustain for it takes effort, but the only love worth living for, for it is this love that transforms and transcends.

It is this love that brings life, that brings us home, to safety, free, knowing we are nothing and yet we are everything for now is the time.

To come back.

To come back to life…